SHAPE UP WITH

THE SUPERSTARS

First published in 1985 by
Richard Drew Publishing Ltd
6 Clairmont Gardens,
Glasgow G3 7LW

ISBN 0 86267 090 X

Copyright © 1985 Townsend Thoresen
Produced in association with
Transworld International (U.K.) Inc.
and
The Eggs Authority

THE SUPERSTARS is the Trade Mark of Candid Productions Inc.

Research and interviews by Antony Kamm and Rita Perry
Further editorial material by Robert Crampsey and John Wilcox
Menus and recipes devised by the Eggs Information Bureau

Typeset by John Swain and Son (Glasgow) Ltd
Printed in Great Britain by
Blantyre Printing and Binding Co. Ltd

The Publisher is grateful to the following who contributed
illustrations.

All Action Photographic	pp 115, 118/119, 120 and 123 Cover photo of Andy Ruffell
All-Sport Photographic	pp 9, 11, 12, 14, 17, 19, 27, 32, 37, 39, 43, 49, 51, 57, 58/59, 63, 65, 69, 73, 85, 86, 88, 92, 93, 105, 106, 109, 112 Cover photos of Neil Adams, Kriss Akabusi, Robin Brew, Garry and Kathy Cook, Annabel Croft, Duncan Goodhew, Gordon Greenidge, Brian Hooper, Bryan Robson.
Barry Bullough	All Food Photography (Props by Way In/Living at Harrods and Descamps of Sloane Street.)
Judo Photos Unlimited	pp 97, 98
Mike Scaddan	pp 7, 20, 25, 40, 47, 67, 83, 117, 125, 126 Cover photos of hockey game and Virginia Holgate.

The Publisher has made every effort to trace the owners of copyright
photographs and where he has failed to do so he will be pleased to make
the necessary arrangements at the first opportunity.

CONTENTS

FOREWORD
BY RON PICKERING

The origins of 'The Superstars' go back to 1948 when the American Olympic Ice Skating Champion Dick Button literally brought a new dimension to his event. The sheer power of his leaps, his agility and his originality were breathtaking, yet he was the first to confess that at school he was far from being the best all-round athlete in his class. Indeed, when he attempted to play baseball or football the rest of the class laughed. This genius on skates knew then that to train with great devotion at one specific sporting skill rarely makes a good all-round performer. Of course there are supreme tests of all round sporting skill and athleticism such as the Modern Pentathlon and the Heptathlon and Decathlon; but nowadays it is accepted that to excel in these events demands exceptional and specialised dedication and ability. However, apart from these specific areas most sportsmen share common ground with competitors from quite different sports. Footballers must run, jump and throw as well as kick with accuracy; every racquet player must have hand and eye co-ordination as well as agility around the court; swimmers need mobility and endurance; and all need speed, strength and stamina together with the ability to maintain their great skills under pressure.

In 1971 Dick Button was impressed by an article in the magazine 'Sports Illustrated' on one Eddie Villella, a leading male dancer in the New York Ballet Company, who was acclaimed for the sheer physical qualities that he brought to the dance. The article related how Villella had been brought up in a downtown area of New York and had graduated from a tough street fighter to a welter-weight boxing champion and a useful baseball player.

Dick Button wondered who, and from which sport, might compare with Villella in all-round ability and fitness. The question was transposed into a contest, bought by ABC television and named The Superstars.

That was in 1972. At roughly the same time by sheer coincidence, I and a group of enthusiastic sportsmen involved in television were gathering together in a Leeds hotel to consider a programme which might involve Britain's sporting celebrities. Since Barney Colehan, David Vine and Eddie Waring were there and all had been successfully involved in 'It's a Knockout', it was felt at first that the flavour should be somewhat similar. Then Don Revie, the Leeds United Manager, pointed out that highly paid and very valuable soccer players could not be put at risk. I, too, was adamant that sport and farce rarely go well together. Lots of ideas were forthcoming and we were still talking when the Americans beat us to the punch with their first television programme. In it I remember that Joe Frazier, the heavyweight boxing champion of the world, nearly drowned in the swimming event and Bob Seagren, the Olympic pole vault champion, won the contest and was suddenly $50,000 richer! We then decided to adopt and adapt the American format for the UK.

It was the summer of 1973 at Crystal Palace that the BBC staged the first British Superstars. Taking part were Bobby Moore (Soccer), Barry John (Rugby), Roger Taylor (Tennis), Tony Jacklin (Golf), David Hemery (Athletics) and Jackie Stewart (Motor Racing). Each competitor was given a choice of eight out of ten events but was excluded from or given a handicap in his own speciality event. The competition was very keen, for they were all champions in their own right with reputations to defend, but there was a lot of fun also and a good spirit of sportsmanship. We tried to keep the events as near as possible to the actual rules of the sport and the accent was on tests that were physically demanding, rather than on highly practised skills. Jackie Stewart, gutsy and aggressive, impressed everyone with his physical fitness and was later backed up by most of the other racing drivers. But the event was won by the Olympic 400 metres hurdles champion and world record holder David Hemery. David, an impoverished student, decided to take the prize money of some £4,000, having retired from amateur athletics, but surprisingly was criticised by some for actually taking money from sport.

Other critics dubbed the programme 'trash sport', claiming that prostitution of pure sport was taking place. The irony here was that many of the same critics spent much of their time writing about the noble art of boxing, or, even worse, the televised version of all-in wrestling! But the television audiences loved it. Soon, 10 million people were viewing regularly, with a one-time peak audience of 16 million. The names and the games changed year by year as first we went into Europe, then started the pastmasters, the women's championship and the juniors before actually building up to the World Championships and

5

Team Superstars. More than 750 great sports personalities have taken part and we have travelled the world from Pine Mountain, Georgia to Christchurch, New Zealand. A rich experience indeed.

Within the overall event there were the individual competitions which became a series of challenges. Who was Britain's fastest soccer player — Mike Channon, or Malcolm Macdonald? Could Rugby Leaguer Del Drummond or Keith Fielding beat the fast men of soccer? Could the great pastmasters like Lynn Davies, John Sherwood, or David Hemery match their younger pretenders? Might the toughness of Brian Jacks equal the astonishing abilities of Canada's Brian Budd and would our great pole vaulter Brian Hooper better the previous exploits of Sweden's Kjell Isacksson or America's Bob Seagren? Excitement ran high in the pubs and clubs up and down the country. Brian Jacks' oranges became a great talking point, as did Jody Schector putting sun oil on his shoes so that he could slip faster during his squat thrusts! Poor Jonah Barrington was almost drummed out of his squash club for showing dissidence, despite an abject apology on a later appearance. Kevin Keegan's courage after his bike crash in 1976 is still talked about in revered tones. Soccer's Stan Bowles is remembered for blowing a hole in the table with his .38 pistol rather than hitting the target and boxing's Alan Minter for canoeing across the course rather than along it. Reputations were rarely dented and so often enhanced. It was the ladies who introduced charm, the juniors incredible potential, the pastmasters the nostalgia, the teams a revitalised excitement of competition. The champions, those qualities which so often match rare gifts with complete dedication. So as we approach ninety programmes spread over twelve years, working with dedicated BBC teams and marvellously enthusiastic sponsors, rubbing shoulders with most of the sporting 'greats' in the world; is it any wonder that David Vine and I are the envy of all those who love sport? Don't tell us how lucky we are — we know!

The pages that follow give a glimpse of that world through the eyes of thirteen talented sportsmen and women: Superstars all. They do more than that, however — they point the way towards achieving a fundamental fitness which must be at the root of any sporting career and which is also the basis of life enjoyment for everybody.

For most of my life I have been intimately concerned with sport and know better than most as a teacher, coach and commentator how close physical fitness is to good health. The Superstars' basic concept of all-round ability and fitness, then, is as relevant to the housewife and bank clerk as it is to the professional athlete.

The tips to simple exercise and diet contained in this book won't exactly create a race of sporting superstars. But, if followed, they may form the basis of physical well-being, so improving quality of life. I wish it well.

NEIL ADAMS

Born: Rugby, 27 September 1958.
Education: Leamington Spa.
World Light Middleweight Judo Champion 1981.
World silver medal 1983.
Olympic silver medal 1980 and 1984.
British Champion — seven times.
European Champion — four times.
Married.
Sports Consultant.

At 26, Britain's judo champion in the 71kg class, Neil Adams, manifests the same composure off the mat as he has always displayed in his distinguished fighting career. This calm, placid person has amassed enough achievements to earn him *The Times'* assessment as 'the greatest judo fighter Britain has ever had.' Judo itself is an aggressive sport but Neil describes it as 'controlled aggression'. 'I have a slow fuse. It takes a lot to get me going. And that's an advantage in judo because it's hard to perform rationally when tempers are lost.' Yet, in the world of combat sports, nothing is certain and favourites in competitions can be upset. It is a mark of Neil's maturity and will to win that he can accept past disappointments and continues to train rigorously for international world class judo competition.

'My father, Cyril, started me in judo. He was involved in it and used to take my older brother and me to the club. Both of us started entering competitions. I won my first junior British competition when I was ten and retained the title for five consecutive years. Dad was my coach until I was about sixteen, though he never forced my brother and me to train or compete. I think a lot of kids in sport today get pushed by their parents — maybe to do what they themselves wanted to do and didn't. But Dad never did and that's probably why we never got fed up with judo.'

Neil left school at sixteen to come down to London to train seriously. And seven years later in 1981, at Maastricht in The Netherlands, he triumphed in style by becoming the first person ever from Britain — as well as the first non-Japanese — to win the World Championship at his weight. 'That was a really exciting moment.' And particularly so, after the 1980 Olympics in Moscow, when he had to content himself with a silver medal

after a controversial decision based on points in the final against Italy's Ezio Gamba.

Favoured to win again in the Los Angeles Olympics four years later, Neil carried the hopes of most of his countrymen to earn the gold. He had won every tournament that year and there was a great deal of pressure. But Neil doesn't seek excuses. 'I went into the final feeling physically drained because I had had some hard fights earlier on, particularly against the Frenchman, Nowak, who is the Rocky Marciano of judo. But I felt confident I was going to win. I had a lapse of concentration and I made a mistake and full credit to Wieneke for making the most of it. The throw was just like an unexpected left hook that knocks you out.'

But for Neil, who is revered even by the Japanese as an outstanding stylist, consistency is the hallmark of a star athlete. 'Someone can always pull off a one-time win, but I most admire athletes who win convincingly again and again over the years — Ed Moses, for example. And in judo, I have a great deal of respect for the Japanese Olympic heavyweight champion, Yasuhiro Yamshita, who hasn't been beaten in nearly three hundred contests since 1977.'

Judo is a physically demanding sport. 'I think it's one of the hardest cardio-vascular sports in the world. When you're grappling face to face with someone, excellent aerobic and muscle conditioning are vital.' Neil's training methods require some three hours of skill training — free fighting and sparring — every day. 'There are a certain number of basic techniques but infinite ways of doing them. So you're thinking all the time too. Weight training concentrates on specific muscle groups, to strengthen and stretch them, and I'll spend an hour a day on that but doing different programmes — cardio-vascular circuits, heavy weights or local endurance circuits.

'Running is an important part of general fitness training. It's not my favourite exercise and I'm happy when I've finished my daily four miles. I like to get it over with first so I usually run early in the day for twenty minutes or so. And I always run in the parks, never in the city.

'If you're starting out, just run as far as you can without losing your breath and then either increase your distance or your speed. You have to con yourself to do it and sometimes it can help to have a friend run with you. But the results are worth it.'

Neil's wife, Alison, a beauty therapist, is an example of the rapid improvement that can be achieved. 'When Alison started running, she could barely go a hundred metres. But she runs three or four times a week and now, after about seven weeks, she can easily run two miles and is even talking about entering a marathon!' Neil's blue eyes twinkle mischieviously. 'And no, I never insisted she run either. She did it all by herself. If you give 100 per cent no matter what level of fitness you're at, you find you just get better and better. The fitter you are, the more effort you can expend — I'm still improving and still sometimes surprise myself at what I can do.'

Alison is the chef in the Adams's household and Neil enthusiastically praises her expertise. He prefers gammon or chicken to steak and is fond of vegetables, particularly cauliflower and sweet corn. 'If you don't eat properly, you just run down. So we always have regular mealtimes at home. But exercise and diet go hand in hand. You've got to balance your intake of food and your output of energy. Someone who's twenty stone and unfit shouldn't start off jogging straightaway. He should lose some weight first by eating less and then begin slowly to take some mild exercise. The more excess weight you lose, though, the fitter you get. And whether you're dieting or getting fit, you shouldn't let it be monotonous. You can vary the form of exercise and the food — salads can be made really tempting and interesting too.'

In The Superstars 1981, Neil came first in the Luton heat. 'Superstars is a lot of fun but it makes a big difference to your results if you can train especially for it. Judo competitions are run year round and when The Superstars final was held that year at Plymouth, I was in training for our world championships. Everybody in The Superstars is a champion of a kind anyway and even though we're competitors, none of the events are your particular sport so there isn't quite the same seriousness. And it is terrific fun. In the cyclo-cross event, eight of us had to run with a bicycle and jump on and off it over obstacles and streams and then get through a two or three foot wide lane with rocks and water in it. At the end, we were all so caked with mud, I don't think my own mother would have recognised me!'

Neil is honorary chief instructor at the Budokwai Club in London where he gives occasional lessons to seniors. 'That's the great thing about judo — you're always learning. You'll find seventy-year-olds on the mat. And of course it attracts a lot of youngsters — 70 per cent of the membership of the British Judo association are kids.' Neil actively supports the association and also helps with the national team. Competitive sport is arduous though. 'I keep to a holding programme of running and weight training just to maintain my conditioning to a certain level. But intensive training — maybe four or five hours every day for weeks or even months — must be done to prepare for a major event.'

Eventually he and Alison would like to run their own training and fitness centre in London, but, for now, Neil has set his sights on winning the next Commonwealth Games and World Championships. The latter will be held in 1985 in Seoul, Korea and they may well provide an interesting first encounter for him with the city which will host the 25th Olympic Games in 1988.

BREAKFAST SCRAMBLE *(Serves 1)*

2 eggs
salt and pepper
15g (½oz) butter
1 tomato, cut into wedges
1 tablespoon cream or milk

Beat eggs and seasoning together. Melt butter in a small saucepan, over a gentle heat. Pour in eggs. Add tomatoes. Keeping a low heat, stir until eggs are softly set. Remove from heat and add cream or milk. Serve at once.

NEIL ADAMS
chose for breakfast

Fresh Grapefruit
Breakfast Scramble
Toast and Marmalade
Tea/Coffee

---

and for lunch

Mushrooms à la Grecque

Cheesey Baked Eggs

Mixed Side Salad

Fresh Fruit

MUSHROOMS À LA GRECQUE *(Serves 4)*

2 tablespoons oil

1 onion, chopped

2 carrots, peeled, diced

1 clove garlic, crushed

1 bay leaf

100ml (4fl oz) white wine

salt and freshly ground black pepper

350g (12oz) small button mushrooms, washed

2 tomatoes, skinned, sliced

chopped parsley

Heat oil in saucepan. Add onion, carrots and garlic. Cook gently until soft but not browned. Add bay leaf, wine and seasoning, bring to boil and simmer for 2 minutes. Add mushrooms and continue to simmer for a further 5 minutes, stirring frequently. Remove bay leaf and allow mixture to cool. Place mushroom mixture in refrigerator to chill. Serve garnished with tomato and chopped parsley.

CHEESEY BAKED EGGS *(Serves 4)*

6 eggs

25g (1oz) butter

50g (2oz) Double Gloucester cheese, grated

salt and pepper

25g (1oz) wholemeal breadcrumbs

a few sesame seeds

Set oven 190°C (375°F) gas mark 5.

Grease 4 individual ovenproof dishes. Separate 4 eggs. Place the yolks and the two whole eggs into a bowl and beat together lightly. Cut butter into small pieces and add to egg mixture. Add cheese, seasoning and breadcrumbs and mix well. Whisk whites to soft peaks and fold into mixture. Divide mixture between dishes and sprinkle with sesame seeds. Bake for 15-20 minutes until risen and golden brown. Serve with salad or new potatoes and green beans.

KRISS AKABUSI

Born: London, 1958.

Education: Edmonton County School.

Europa Cup gold medal 4×400m, 1983.

Olympic silver medal 4×400m, 1984.

Married, one daughter.

Sergeant, Army PT Corps.

Britain's number one 400 metres runner is strong, beautifully built, and has just the right combination of modesty and ambition to enable him to succeed at the highest level in this most punishing of the sprints. Yet he never ran a race at any distance until after he left school!

At school, Kriss played football and basketball. He joined the Army from school, and began to do a bit of cross-country running. But during PT, running endlessly round the track in the hanger that was used as a gym, he discovered that he could go flat out farther and faster than the others. Being of easy disposition, he was readily persuaded to try 400 metre running. Two Army junior championship wins at the distance, and then a senior win, simply confirmed how right his mentors had been. Indeed, while still a junior, Kriss came second to the international runner Walcott Taylor in the senior event.

Though he ran competitively at club level when he was stationed in Germany, Kriss was virtually unknown to the public in UK until 1983. A second place in that year's national championships brought him a place in Britain's 4×400 metres relay team for the World Championships ... and disappointment. His strength was a factor in his helping his team through the heats and semi-final, but he was dropped from the final in favour of his friend Ainsley Bennett, on the day a faster but not necessarily a stronger runner. The result, however, was a bronze medal for the British team, and one also for Kriss for his efforts in the earlier rounds.

That first taste of the limelight fired him. 'Once I'd been there and I'd savoured what it was like to run in a major championship, I felt I could make the 1984 Olympic team — and that is what I aimed for,' is how he puts it. Even so, he confesses that as far back as 1979 he had fostered secret ambitions of being in that team. 'While it wasn't something I properly entertained, in sport you've got to aim high and set yourself goals beyond those you think you can achieve.'

He duly made the relay team for the Los Angeles Olympics and also, as what he regards as a bonus, he got a place in the individual 400 metres, in which he reached the semi-finals. His real ambition was to run in the relay final. Britain's silver medal in that race, behind the Americans, in which each member of the team — Kriss, Garry Cook, Todd Bennett and Phil Brown, ran virtually the race of his life, is a part of British Olympic history. Yet Kriss's best personal moment so far, and possibly an even greater achievement on the part of that same team, came a year earlier.

Just a week after being dropped from the World Championship finals, Kriss was recalled by the Board to run first leg in the 4×400 metres relay in the Europa Cup finals, against the mighty Russians, the world champions, and East Germans. It was the last event of the day, before a packed home crowd of 17,000 who had come hopefully to see British successes. Kriss handed over in third place behind Russia and East Germany, as had been expected. Yet Garry, Todd and Phil, running brilliantly, pulled back the deficit not only to win the gold medal, but also to beat the UK All-Comers record and move the British men's team up from fourth to third in the overall championship.

It was a heady moment for Kriss. 'Everyone was going wild. And there I was, with the other three the centre of attraction. As

The Superteams 1985 — studies in determination and concentration.

20

we carried round the Union Jack, I felt . . . I want more of this. I want to stay at this level.'

To Kriss, 'this level' means staying Britain's top 400 metres runner for the next few years, and perhaps winning individual medals in the European championships and the Commonwealth Games in 1986. However, before that is another personal goal — to represent Europe against USA, Oceania and Africa in the World Cup in Canberra in October 1985. To achieve this, he must first be selected as Britain's single representative in the individual 400 metres in the Europa Cup, and then be one of the first six in the final.

Kriss will run 15 to 20 serious 400 metres races in a season. In between them, he concentrates on speed training. He might do three 200 metre sprints flat out with ten minutes rest between each, to allow his body completely to recover — for a school or club runner, he recommends four 60 metre sprints with seven minutes rest between each.

Winter is the time for building up power and strength. First, he allows himself three weeks rest to let any lingering aches and pains heal up. During this time he will do nothing more strenuous than basketball or playing tennis with his wife, Monika, a stunning blonde sports teacher whom he met when he was stationed in Germany. Then comes six weeks' daily jogging, getting the heart and legs ready to move again. After that, work begins in earnest. There will be weight-lifting for strength, and circuit training to get the heart, lungs and muscles in trim — up to ten exercises for thirty seconds, one after the other with twenty seconds rest between each: press-ups, sit-ups, squat-thrusts, hopping, leaping, jumping. The aim is to push the body and its organs just that much farther than they will have to go in the races in summer. Hill-running is another valuable form of the same kind of training — legs and heart have to learn how to beat resistance so that racing on the flat becomes more like cruising.

This, Kriss suggests, is the kind of winter schedule any aspiring runner should aim at. For general fitness, whatever your age, he recommends first a mixture of jogging and walking 'round the block' for two or three miles. Then gradually build up the proportion of running. Only when you can run the whole of your distance with ease, should you increase it, and then only if you want to do so.

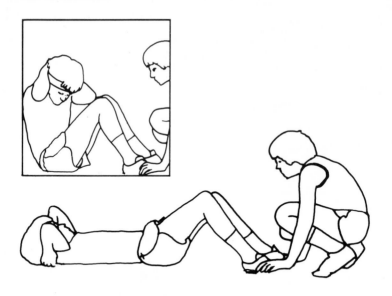

Apart from running, he advocates sit-ups as an exercise for general fitness. 'The first things to go are the stomach muscles,' he explains sagely. 'Anchor your feet under a bed or couch — or get someone to hold them down for you. If you can't do one sit-up properly, don't try. Just raise your trunk and shoulders a few inches each time. At the beginning, it's better to do ten of these, than to struggle to do one proper sit-up. After a month of daily mini-sit-ups, then try the proper kind again, until you can do five, one after the other . . . and ultimately ten.'

Kriss himself has no weight problems — he burns up so many calories in training. But he is careful about not eating too many potatoes. His diet includes plenty of egg dishes: 'Eggs are a good source of iron, which you need especially when you are training hard. For if you don't have enough iron in your system then, you'll get ill!' Breakfast for Kriss may be cereals (for roughage), scrambled eggs on toast, and orange juice (for vitamin C). He will only have a light lunch if he is training at 5 o'clock. His main meal of the day is in the evening — with meat or fish and two vegetables, one of which will always be fresh.

Home for the Akabusis and their small daughter is near where Kriss's Army duties take him. It is now a tiny semi-detached house near the Hampshire coast, where Monika brings a taste of her native country to the family cooking.

KRISS AKABUSI
chose for dinner

Corn on the Cob
Seafood Wraps
Green Salad
Fresh Fruit

SEAFOOD WRAPS *(Serves 4)*
FILLING

25g (1oz) butter

350g (12oz) white fish eg haddock or cod cut into largish chunks

175g (6oz) peeled prawns

3 spring onions, cut into thin strips

50g (2oz) beansprouts

salt and pepper

WRAPS

8 eggs

8 teaspoons cold water

salt and pepper

50g (2oz) butter

For filling, melt butter in a frying pan. Add fish and cook over a moderate heat until cooked through. Add prawns, onions and beansprouts and cook for a further 4-5 minutes until beansprouts have softened. Season to taste. Keep warm.

For Wraps, heat in 20cm-23cm (8"-9") omelette pan gently. Break eggs into a bowl, add water, seasoning and beat lightly together. Add a little of the butter to the pan, turn up heat and when butter begins to sizzle but not brown, pour in $\frac{1}{4}$ of egg mixture to coat base of pan. Cook until set on top and lightly browned on underside. Slide out of pan and keep warm. Repeat, making 3 more wraps with remaining mixture. Divide filling between wraps and either fold into 4 or roll up. Serve immediately garnished with whole prawns and lemon wedges.

Serve with spicy sauce and green side salad.

MONIKA AKABUSI'S
WESTPHALIAN SPINACH SCRAMBLED EGG
(Serves 4)

900g (2lb) fresh spinach, chopped

1 large onion, chopped

1 teaspoon ground nutmeg

1 level tablespoon oatmeal

8 eggs

salt and pepper

25g (1oz) butter

2 tablespoons milk

2 medium-sized potatoes per person, boiled, kept warm

Mix together spinach, onion, nutmeg and oatmeal. Place in saucepan with sufficient water to cover. Bring to the boil and simmer for 30 minutes. Beat eggs and seasoning together. Melt butter in a saucepan over a gentle heat. Pour in eggs. Keeping a low heat, stir until eggs are softly set. Remove from heat and add milk.

Place potatoes on individual plates and roughly break them up with a fork. Divide spinach mixture into 4 and place on top of potatoes. Finally top with scrambled eggs.

ROBIN BREW

Born: Portsmouth, 28 June 1962.

Education: Kelly College, Devon.

*Silver medal, 200m Individual Medley,
Commonwealth Games, Brisbane, 1982 (British Record).*

*Fourth, 200m Individual Medley, Olympic Games,
Los Angeles, 1984 and Captain, GB Swimming Team.*

Married.

Physical Training Instructor, RAF Halton.

A quiet man, Robin Brew has a boyish charm which underlines his genuine modesty about his impressive achievements in swimming against stiff international competition. That he was invited to captain the Great Britain swimming team at the 24th Olympic Games was an acknowledgment of his intense but low-key patriotism and his highly-developed sense of sportsmanship. For as a promising swimmer in 1980, he declined several offers from American universities (with their attendant financial security and glamorous prospects) to remain in the more uncertain, certainly less lucrative world of competitive swimming in the UK.

Nor is it unusual that Robin joined the RAF when he was 18 and is now a Corporal, working full time as a physical training instructor at Halton, Bucks, combining his love of swimming with his strong interest in general fitness training. Robin's father, Archie Brew, was a Chief Petty Officer in the Royal Navy and was himself keenly interested in water sports, especially waterpolo. It was while the Brew family was stationed in Singapore that his father encouraged seven-year-old Robin to learn to swim.

'In Singapore, school finished at 1 pm and it was so hot and humid that we all used to go to the pool. One day, I was watching my dad swim up and down and I just jumped in. Dad stopped and said, "What are you doing?" And I told him: "I'm doing what you're doing!"'

Robin began to take lessons and gradually worked his way through bronze, silver and gold swimming survival awards — perhaps subconsciously motivated by his certain knowledge that very large Portuguese men-of-war lurked in the warm waters of the Java Sea!

When the family was posted back to the UK, 11-year-old Robin joined the Portsmouth Northsea Swimming Club and

first encountered competitive swimming. 'I enjoyed going away with the team on weekends and I also liked the competitions. It becomes an on-going thing really: you train and improve and do better in the events. I've been very lucky in having good coaches and lots of support from my Dad though he certainly never pressured me into it. I think your own desire comes through and you understand what you're training for and you try to realise your potential.'

The highwater mark for a talented swimmer is a chance to compete for his country against the best in the world in the Olympic Games and, in 1984, Robin realised his dream. 'There's a lot at stake in the Olympics. You're representing your country and you don't want to let anybody down. It was lots of fun but also one point in your life when you want everything to go right. As captain, I wanted to boost morale, to get each member of the team involved in the experience of others. Ultimately, though, swimming is an individual sport and you just have to get out there and do your best.'

Robin posted the second fastest qualifying time in a new British record of 2.04.13, and, in the final, missed a medal by a mere 2/100 of a second.

Robin's event, the 200m individual medley, is made up of four consecutive 50m distances using the butterfly, back, breast and freestyle strokes. Which is hardest? 'The butterfly is technically the most difficult but by the time the freestyle comes up, you can be pretty tired and it's not so easy either.' Especially when you are aiming at target times of 27, 32, 35 and 28 seconds respectively for each leg.

Why did he choose the medley in the first place? 'I could do each stroke well but I knew I'd never be the best in any one of them, and I wanted to be the best at something.'

Each part of the medley calls for the use of different sets of muscles: the breast stroke, for example, is probably best suited to a tall, muscular person — the powerful upper body pulls the swimmer through the water aided by strong drives from the legs; the butterfly, on the other hand, needs a long, loose supple body with great flexibility. The 200m medley places a lot of emphasis on overall strength while its sister event, the 400m (where each of the four strokes is performed for twice the distance) requires stamina to stay the course. Pace — the timing and rhythm of each stroke and smooth transitions between

To a record! Robin on his way to breaking Andy Ruffell's Superteams' bar jump record in 1985.

them — is important in the medley, whatever the distance.

To build up the strength he needs for his event (and unlike many swimmers), Robin finds running is a good exercise for him. 'It's an aerobic exercise which I particularly enjoy. Feeling fit is important to me but I don't do any set programme. I just run when I want to, for different distances, sometimes five or ten or even twenty miles at once. Being fit has always had a high priority with me and my job gets me involved with a lot of general exercise.

'Motivation is a big part of teaching so if someone is doing step-ups and I see him slowing down, I'll run over and demonstrate the speed I want him to maintain. It doesn't mean I do every exercise with the trainees, but instructors do have to run around a lot. The facilities at Halton are quite comprehensive. We have two gymnasiums, each holding different courts for badminton, basketball, etc., outdoor pitches for soccer or rugby, an outdoor track and indoor swimming pool. I usually give four double lessons a day, two before lunch and two after. Classes are diverse too; some apprentices are in their late teens and other students who are upgrading their qualifications may be in their 30s or 40s. Each day is different, depending on the group and also where we are in the syllabus. So I could be teaching swimming, then rugby, then volley-ball and then doing PT exercises.

'For someone just starting to get fit, though, moderation and control is most important. That's true of whatever exercise you choose. You shouldn't just go to a squash court suddenly one day after years of doing no exercise and play a game — you can really hurt yourself. When you start to jog for instance, you should begin very gently on grass, not concrete. Swimming is also a gentle way to get your body aware of doing something physical. It exercises a range of different muscles and the buoyancy of the water helps you to exert yourself without strain. Very few people ever injure themselves swimming.

'Light bench-press exercises — even just going through the motions with a 10 pound bar weight — are another good way to get your body used to doing some kind of exercise.'

Robin participated in The Superstars 1985 championships. 'It was great fun and a real challenge to compete against other athletes in different sports. If there was any skill involved, however, I didn't do very well. In the shooting event for example,

you had to run 800m and then shoot at five targets. For every one you missed, you picked up ten penalty points. I figured I only had a 50/50 chance of hitting the target anyway, even if I took my time aiming, so I just ran flat out and fired off all five shots within 15 seconds.' And did he hit the targets? 'Not one,' he laughs uproariously.

1984 was a milestone year for Robin. In September, he married Lynn whom he had met at school nine years before. Petite and vivacious, Lynn is a Registered Nurse with both General and Sick Children's qualifications. The Brews live in Dunstable, close to both RAF Halton and Luton and Dunstable General Hospital where Lynn is on staff.

One of Lynn's many talents is that she is an excellent cook. Robin ruefully admits to a limited expertise with soups, cereals, fried eggs and his *pièce de résistance* — toast! Lynn's culinary skill is more than adequate, however, for she effortlessly produces well-balanced, nutritious repasts. Chinese food, with its emphasis on fresh vegetables and contrasting tastes and textures is a favourite for both Brews, and a wok, a wedding present from a thoughtful friend, hangs prominently in their kitchen.

Soft-spoken and gentle in manner, Robin is a fine example of the sportsman. His next big challenge is the Commonwealth Games to be held in Edinburgh in 1986 — a special significance for him because his father was born in Scotland. But whether he wins, loses or draws, Robin Brew is, in every sense of the word a Superstar.

31

BAKED PRAWN AVOCADO *(Serves 4)*

40g (1½oz) butter
40g (1½oz) flour
250ml (½pt) milk
½ teaspoon curry powder (medium strength)
100g (4oz) prawns
1 small green apple, cored, chopped
2 ripe avocados
little lemon juice
15g (½oz) breadcrumbs

Set oven 180°C (350°F) gas mark 4.

Place butter, flour and milk in a saucepan, bring to the boil, whisking continuously until sauce is thick and smooth. Simmer for 2 minutes. Remove from heat, add curry powder, prawns and apple. Cut avocados in half lengthwise, remove stone and cut out a little flesh to make room for the filling. Sprinkle a little lemon juice over cut surface of avocados. Pile prawn mixture on top of each avocado half and place in a heat-proof dish. Sprinkle breadcrumbs on top and bake for 20-25 minutes. Serve garnished with watercress.

CREAMY PASTA SPECIAL *(Serves 4)*

50g (2oz) butter or herb butter

225g (8oz) noodles, pasta shapes or spaghetti, freshly cooked

100g (4oz) peas, cooked

175g (6oz) ham, cut into thin strips

6 eggs

200ml (8fl oz) milk, single cream or natural yoghurt

salt and freshly ground black pepper

Parmesan cheese, grated

Heat butter in a large saucepan, add pasta and allow to heat through, shaking pan frequently. Add peas and ham, stir well and cook slowly for a few minutes. Beat eggs, milk and seasoning together. Pour over pasta and cook slowly, stirring until egg just sets. Sprinkle with cheese and serve immediately with a mixed salad.

FRUIT WHIP

Lighten puréed fruit by folding in 2 whisked egg whites per 225g (8oz) to make a quick and easy dessert.

GARRY AND KATHY COOK

Garry:
Born: Wednesbury, 10 January 1958.
Education: Borough Road College.
European Championships 1982, 4th in 800m and silver medal 4×400m.
Commonwealth Games 1982, gold medal 4×400m.
World Championships 1983, bronze medal 4×400m.
Olympic Games 1984, silver medal 4×400m.
1982 World Record 4×800m relay.
Married.
Manager, Alexander Sports Stadium, Birmingham.

Kathy:
Born: Winchester, 3 May 1960.
Education: Borough Road College.
Commonwealth Games 1978, gold medal 4×100m.
Olympic Games 1980, bronze medal 4×100m.
World Cup 1981, silver medal 100 metres.
Commonwealth Games 1982, silver medal 200 metres, gold medal 4×100m.
World Championships 1983, 3rd 200 metres and 2nd 4×100m.
Olympic Games 1984, bronze medal 400 metres and 4×100m.
Married.
Liaison Officer, TSB Bank.

Garry and Kathy Cook have each displayed outstanding ability in their chosen events — middle-distance and sprints respectively — as well as in relays. Married two years ago, Garry and Kathy have known each other since the late 1970s and, despite rigorous training schedules and necessary career commitments, they have both been dedicated to, and high achievers in, track athletics. Athletics, in fact, has been a part of their lives since they were teenagers.

Garry used to play virtually every sport when he was at

school, 'but in the summer, it was mainly athletics. When I was about twelve, my PE teacher took about four of us to meet the athletics' coach at Wolverhampton. I guess we must have shown some potential in inter-school meets and he thought we could benefit from special coaching. He used to drive us over for training sessions three times a week while we were going to school. Joining the club was good because if you're good in inter-school matches it's easy to become complacent, and lots of good competition with a club really brings you down to earth.'

Kathy also joined a local club when she was about thirteen. 'I was best in my school but I really just enjoyed track. After I joined the club, though, I started to train more seriously and began to think that this was something I could do really well.'

How did they discover the distance that best suited them? 'I got into middle-distance events by trial and error really,' says Garry. 'I think that youngsters should try a bit of everything — you don't always know what you're best at. Look at Steve Ovett, for instance — world record-holder at 1500 metres but at National Schools level, he was running 400 metre races.' Kathy agrees: 'I was interested in the high jump but I met a sprint coach who was available to help me. I don't think it does any harm to try for lots of different events even when you're quite old, because you will have had a basic training that works for all of them. Lots of young kids get set into a mould and never try other things. Club level is good because it gives kids a chance at different events.'

The track season runs from April to September though there are indoor meets from January to March. Garry and Kathy have different training routines for winter and summer. 'In winter,' says Garry, 'we look to build up stamina and strength. So I do a lot of long runs, maybe ten miles or so in the park or ten 400 metre runs round the track with a minute's rest in between. I also do some weight training and gym work — sit-ups and push-ups — generally to build up strength. The emphasis in summer training is on speed, so I'll do sprints against the clock.' For winter training, Kathy also does leg-strengthening exercises. 'Hopping on one leg is good because you're using your own body weight. Wearing a weighted jacket makes it even harder. I also do circuits and weight-training similar to Garry's but I don't run quite as far and I have a bit more recovery time in bet-

The Superteams 1985 — the Cooks at play!

ween. And in summer, I'll work on speed as well and also practice starts. It's important for a sprinter to have a good start and I'll work on different techniques. Being tall, it's a difficult area for me, being all crunched up in the start. Smaller, more compact sprinters usually have better starts.' Kathy also does harness work. 'It's just like a harness you put on and your partner gets behind you and holds on. You run and pull him along. It's pretty hard work.'

General fitness has advantages. 'When I first started training,' says Kathy, 'I used to be very ill because I really wasn't fit in those days. We usually have the month of October off and it's hard getting back into a training routine again. But it's good motivation to have a club to go to because there are other people around you working out or training.'

'Fitness pays off healthwise too,' says Garry. 'We don't get as many colds or bouts of 'flu as other people and we seem to shake them off faster. If you want to get fit, though, you should pick something you like doing. Running or swimming are probably best for cardio-vascular fitness but even walking briskly for regular periods can make a difference. Don't run if you absolutely hate it, but sometimes you have to choose an alternative exercise because the facilities just aren't available. At least running doesn't require a lot of equipment. But everybody's more aware today of health and fitness. A few years ago, when I'd go running in the park, I wouldn't see anyone else. Now, there's not just athletes but ordinary people running too. And, here at the stadium, I've noticed a lot of businessmen will come over at lunchtime to run a few laps around the track.'

Kathy works part-time in the marketing department of the TSB head office. Flexible hours means she usually prepares the meals though she cheerfully asserts, 'Garry taught me everything I know!' Traditional eaters, the Cooks have a substantial breakfast, a light lunch and a cooked meal in the evenings. Omelettes are favoured by both because they are quick and easy and full of protein. 'We do have full meals but I think that's better because then you don't snack at other times,' says Kathy. 'If I have lunch at the bank, the other girls — who are usually dieting — laugh when I pull out my packet of sandwiches and say, "Here comes the Olympic diet again!" But we do burn up a lot of calories because we're training several hours a day, seven days a week.'

Kathy was in The Superstars in 1980. 'It was right at the end of the season, so I didn't train specifically for it. I went to the swimming pool a couple of times because I can hardly swim and did manage to swim the distance. I enjoyed the events, though. In the archery event, you had to put your own arrow in the bow and I thought I was doing OK until someone told me that I'd put the arrow in backwards! And then when I did get it right, only one of my arrows hit the target — the rest just skimmed along the ground. Except for the one that hit the cameraman!'

Garry won The Superstars 1983. 'I was pretty surprised to win, but none of the eight competitors had been in Superstars before and no-one had trained specifically for it. Our results weren't as good as some in previous years but it was exciting because five or six people could have won it. It's lots of fun but all sportsmen are competitive and the events were taken seriously. The cycling event was tough and I thought I'd do well in it, but cycling uses a lot of muscles from the knee up and running emphasises the calf muscles. So when I had finished, my legs were pretty wobbly and shaky. I did come first in the sprinting but that was all down to my coach!' He smiles at Kathy.

Besides posting outstanding times in their individual distances, both Garry and Kathy run in relay events. 'Even in club teams or national teams, athletics is an individual event,' says Garry. 'You're running for yourself and that's an extra pressure.' 'Relays are a strange situation,' adds Kathy, 'because the members of the relay team could have been rivals a few hours before. But when you're a part of a team, you work together.' Garry adds, 'At the last Olympics, where we won a silver, if you'd looked at our four best times on a sheet of paper, by rights we shouldn't even have made the final! But I think you're more relaxed as part of a team effort and you can bring out the best in each other.'

'We're fortunate,' says Kathy, 'to have had the chance to do relays. Great Britain has such a good record in relay-running that the positions are keenly contested. You have to pick out your priorities and check the timetables carefully. There's a limit to what you can do.'

The Olympics have always had a special appeal for both Garry and Kathy. 'I can remember,' says Kathy, 'when I was really little, watching the Games and thinking to myself "I'd like to get there".' And like many sportsmen, track athletes feel the pressures of time. 'By your late twenties, it gets more difficult and you're competing with lots of younger people who are at their peak,' says Garry. 'It's also very chancy because you could train hard all winter and then pull a muscle and be out the entire season. The slightest little tear can put you out, because you have to be able to give 100 per cent.'

And marriage between two world class athletes? 'On the whole, there are more advantages than disadvantages,' says Kathy. 'Time is the crucial thing and we are able to train together. We rarely go out and if we have an evening off, we usually just stay at home together. Most times, there just don't seem to be enough hours in the day.'

KATHY COOK
chose for breakfast

Fresh Fruit Juice

Muesli

Scotch Pancakes with Poached Egg

Wholemeal Toast

Coffee

GARRY
chose for dinner

Egg and Avocado Starter

Vegetable Pasta Layer
Mixed Salad

Yoghurt Mallow

SCOTCH PANCAKES *(Serves 4)*

175g (6oz) self-raising flour

pinch salt

½ teaspoon baking powder

25g (1oz) butter

2 eggs

50g (2oz) mature Cheddar cheese, grated

½ teaspoon dry mustard

125ml (¼pt) milk

4 eggs, poached

Sift flour, salt and baking powder into a bowl. Rub in butter. Add the 2 eggs, cheese, mustard and half the milk. Beat ingredients together, gradually adding rest of milk. The mixture should just drop from the spoon when ready. Heat a griddle or thick based frying pan, rub over with lard. When quite hot drop a heaped tablespoon of batter on to griddle. Cook for 3-4 minutes each side. Mixture should make 8 pancakes. Place 2 pancakes on each plate and top with a poached egg. Serve immediately garnished with tomato wedges and watercress.

EGG AND AVOCADO STARTER *(Serves 4)*

4 eggs, hard-boiled, sliced

2 avocados, peeled, sliced

8 radishes, sliced

Arrange egg, avocado and radishes on serving dish. Sprinkle with chopped chives. Serve with yoghurt-watercress dressing.

VEGETABLE PASTA LAYER *(Serves 4)*

225g (8oz) carrots

225g (8oz) courgettes

1 onion

100g (4oz) green pepper, de-seeded

100g (4oz) leek

1 chicken stock cube

25g (1oz) butter

2 level tablespoons flour

250ml (½pt) milk

175g (6oz) Red Leicester cheese, grated

salt and freshly ground black pepper

175g (6oz) green lasagne

Set oven at 190°C (375°F) gas mark 5.

Thinly slice all vegetables. Place in a saucepan with the stock cube and 125ml (¼pt) boiling water. Bring to boil, cover and simmer for about 10 minutes. Melt butter in a saucepan over a gentle heat. Add flour and cook for a few minutes. Gradually add milk, keeping mixture smooth. Bring to the boil and continue to cook, stirring continuously, until mixture thickens. Add 100g (4oz) cheese and seasoning to taste. Meanwhile prepare lasagne according to the instructions on the packet. Divide vegetables between 4 individual heatproof dishes. Top with lasagne, pour over sauce, sprinkle with remaining cheese. Bake for about 20-25 minutes until golden brown.

YOGHURT MALLOW *(Serves 4)*

Fold 2 stiffly whisked egg whites into a small carton of fruit flavoured yoghurt. Spoon into individual dishes. Sprinkle with chopped nuts. Serve within half an hour.

ANNABEL CROFT

Born: London, 12 July 1966.

Education: Westheath, Sevenoaks, Kent.

Junior Wimbledon Title 1984.

Member British team, 1984 Wightman Cup.

Australian Open Junior Title 1984.

Single.

Professional tennis player.

The crowd who shook the Victorian mouldings of the Albert Hall one evening in early November 1984 had something to shout about. Not only was a young British girl beating a hardened American tennis pro in only her second Wightman Cup, but she was displaying a brand of feminine athleticism not seen since the heyday of the young Virginia Wade.

Annabel Croft went on to beat Alycia Moulton to give Great Britain an outside chance of winning a trophy which has become as American as hominy grits. It was too good to last, of course, and the USA retained the trophy. But 18-year-old Annabel had made her mark.

That night, in front of television cameras and a crowd whose noisy enthusiasm made their formal evening dress look incongruous, she revealed a formidable range of ground strokes and prodigious stamina. The display capped a year of great achievement for Annabel; a year which saw her adopt a planned regimen of physical training, become Junior Wimbledon champion, Australian Open Junior champion, and rise in world tennis rankings from 190 to 56.

It was not, of course, always so.

Annabel Croft started playing at eight years old while on holiday with her family in Marbella, Spain. After coaching by the local club professional, she entered a junior tournament and lost to a nine-year-old boy. When the family returned to England, her mother arranged for Annabel's older brother, Simon, to join a group coached by Pauline Cox. Annabel wanted to play too, though her brother's fraternal assessment — 'She's no good. She lost to a nine-year-old in Spain.' — reduced young Annabel to tears. But Pauline Cox agreed to give Annabel private lessons and a year later, she entered the Kent Junior Tournament. Unfortunately, Annabel drew the top seed as her first opponent and lost 6-0, 6-0. Those early defeats only made her more determined and after playing many more tournaments, she won the national under-12's title.

Annabel entered further competitions, steadily improving her game. At the age of 17, she underwent a harsh test when, deputising for an ailing Anne Hobbs, she partnered Jo Durie against Martina Navratilova and Pam Shriver in the 1983 Wightman Cup.

At Wimbledon in 1984, she beat the Swiss girl, Petra Delhees 6-3, 6-0, and then the American, Michelle Torres, in a marathon match 6-3, 2-6, 7-5. The third round found her in the public eye on number one court, playing against Chris Evert-Lloyd, who is a kind of heroine to Annabel. Nor was she disgraced. She took seven games, and each one was hard won and well earned.

To cap this she went on to win the Junior Wimbledon title, the first British player to do so since 1956, without losing a set until the final.

Then came a set-back when nothing seemed to go right on the circuit and the young Kentish girl took a short break to take stock and review her career. It was cross-roads time. Annabel decided to apply herself to attaining a degree of fitness which had eluded her before.

The very internationalism of the women's professional tennis circuit itself poses physical problems for an athlete: so many hours spent sitting in aeroplanes, and limousines. Annabel is coached by Australian Owen Davidson in Houston, USA and by Davis Cup player John Feaver in the UK, but she decided to seek additional help in England from Ron Murray, the British National high jump coach, at Crystal Palace. The tennis practice and specific drills supplied by her tennis coaches on either side of the Atlantic were supplemented by a strict regimen from Murray based on multi-gym and weight work.

Now, she works out six days a week as well as playing tennis for two or three hours every day. The benefit, she believes, has been clear and immediate.

Her favourite apparatus is the multi-gym, similar to the American-manufactured Nautilus. 'Working out on the multi-gym tones and strengthens the muscles. You don't get big, bulging muscles unless you lift really heavy weights. I only lift light weights but with lots of repetitions. And I do free weights as well once a week.

'Free weights are good for you to do once a week because even if you only lift a few pounds, you have to balance and control the bars.' Strong arms and chest muscles are important for

Annabel in action during her victory in the Wightman Cup, 1984: and in earnest discussion between games with team captain and coach, Virginia Wade.

a tennis player and bench presses where you lie on your back and push the weights up from your chest are particularly suited to developing the upper body.

Diet is also important to a professional on the year-round tennis circuit. 'Since I started working out on the multi-gym and lifting weights, I've actually lost about seven pounds — without even trying. I stick to pretty basic high-protein, low-fat food with lots of fresh fruit and vegetables. Every day I breakfast on half a grapefruit and a boiled or scrambled egg with plain wholemeal toast and a cup of coffee. I try to control my sweet tooth. Nut meringues and zabaglione are favourites of mine. I save them as special treats.'

In September 1984, Annabel participated in The Superteams

for the Townsend Thoresen Trophy. 'It was great fun meeting a lot of other people in different kinds of sports and finding out their training methods. One of the events involved each team swimming (in wetsuits and with life-jackets) from the dock out to a capsized life raft, righting it and climbing in. Somehow I got hooked on to the side of it and ended up with my bottom in the air, dangling over the side, and unable to move. Needless to say, our side lost that event.'

The fun of competing in The Superstars was a welcome diversion in a year which saw Annabel become a dedicated athlete determined to make her way in one of the most competitive professions in the world. Following her good Wimbledon, Annabel was a prime selection for the 1984 Wightman Cup team, competing against a team captained by her idol, Chris Evert-Lloyd.

After Annabel's exciting win in the singles, Chris commented: 'She is a good player who moves well and has great ground strokes. She also handled her nerves very well here.'

Annabel herself pays tribute to the support she received throughout the tournament from her own captain and coach on the court, Virginia Wade. She also, however, knows well that she could not have brought those dinner-jacketed spectators to their feet cheering like Promenaders if it had not been for the hours spent doing lifts and squats in the gymnasium.

'When I look back, that physical training has really made a difference. The results show: I feel well and I'm playing well. It's tiring but it's great fun and worth it. Now I just want to keep on doing my best and working to improve my game.'

Annabel believes that a basic standard of all-round fitness can be achieved by most people and that you don't have to be a professional athlete to experience the sense of well-being that regular exercise can bring. She pays equal attention, however, to her diet.

Her cooking efforts are limited by her busy training and playing schedule. Her mother, a keen tennis player herself, prepares the family's meals at home with a careful eye on attractively presented nutritious meals. Annabel is conscientious about her diet: one of her favourite dinner menus reflects this — poached salmon with asparagus, petits pois, new potatoes and cucumber salad.

It is, of course, the kind of meal of which champions could well be made. . . .

MRS CROFT'S SPANISH OMELETTE *(Serves 4)*

2 tablespoons olive oil

1 large onion, sliced

3 medium-sized potatoes, cooked, sliced

50g (2oz) mushrooms, sliced

2 tomatoes, peeled, sliced

6 eggs

6 teaspoons cold water

salt and pepper

little oregano

Heat oil in a 20cm-23cm (8″-9″) omelette pan. Add onion and potatoes and cook gently until onion is soft and potato heated through, stirring occasionally. Add mushrooms and tomatoes and cook for a further 3-4 minutes. Break eggs into a bowl, add water, seasoning and oregano, beat lightly together. Pour over vegetable mixture. With a spatula draw cooked egg from edge of pan to the centre so that the liquid egg runs to base of pan and cooks. While the top is still slightly runny, place pan under a hot grill until top is set and browned. Serve cut into wedges with a side salad of green and red lettuce (Radicchio), cucumber and Kenya beans.

ANNABEL CROFT'S FAVOURITE PUDDING ZABAGLIONE *(Serves 4)*

6 egg yolks

50g (2oz) caster sugar

5 tablespoons Marsala

Place egg yolks, caster sugar and Marsala in a medium-sized bowl. Whisk over a pan of simmering water until thick and creamy. Pour into 4 dessert glasses and serve immediately with ratafia biscuits.

DUNCAN GOODHEW

Born: London, 27 May 1957.

Education: Millfield School and North Carolina State University.

British Champion 100m breaststroke, 1978, 1979, 1980.

British Commonwealth Record Holder 1980.

Gold medal at Amersfoort, Paris and Coca Cola Internationals 1980.

Olympic Games 1980, gold medal.

Married.

Businessman and sports consultant.

Britain's first gold medallist at the Moscow Olympics and captain of our swimming team might have had a startlingly different career were it not for a single event in 1962. 'We had a grass tennis court at home in Sussex. But when I was about five years old, a huge digger appeared one day and started to excavate. To me, it was a huge monster and I kept running away from it. Little did I know then that I'd spend most of my life in holes like the one being dug — or that when Wimbledon came round, I'd have pangs of regret and wish my father had left the tennis court there!' Duncan Goodhew laughs impishly for he has had a most remarkable career in those 'holes in the ground' and along the way has triumphed handsomely over some daunting adversities.

'I was a late starter really. My family taught me to swim in that pool but I spent two years in flippers. When I went to Windlesham House in 1965, I decided to make the big move and took the flippers off. The swimming teacher there, Tony Roberts, taught me the breaststroke in about 45 minutes. I guess I had a natural aptitude for it — your joints need to bend in the right way — but if you have that, it's not a difficult stroke. I really wasn't very good but we mucked around a lot in the pool. I suppose I had a raw talent, like two arms and two legs.'

In 1970 he went to Millfield. 'We had two-hour sessions five times a week. About a year after I'd started school there, the Australian Nigel Johnson turned up to train for the 200 metre breaststroke. He was 19 and I was 14. One day when we were both in the pool, I decided to see if I could keep up with him. I didn't, of course, but that night when my schoolmates and I were talking, I suddenly announced, "I'm going to the Olympic Games". And they all laughed.'

His stated ambition must have seemed an impossible dream, for Duncan wasn't top of the form academically or socially. An accidental fall from a tree when he was ten had damaged a nerve and caused all his hair to fall out inside a year. In class, he had fallen two years behind his age group because of unrecognised dyslexia. 'I couldn't read the questions or write the answers even though I knew the material.' He compensated the taunts and jeers of his peers by being aggressive and rebellious. 'I was wretched. I felt frustrated and lacked confidence but I knew from hanging around with my older brother and his friends that I could communicate and get on with people.' The problem was diagnosed, and resolved. 'I'd arrived at Millfield a broken person. They helped put the pieces together.'

Duncan's father was equally supportive and perceptive. 'My father didn't talk much but once, in the very trough of my despair and torments, he said to me, "My boy, just remember your name is Goodhew and be proud of it."' Duncan was devoted to his father — 'He was a God to me' — and though he died in 1972, Duncan feels 'his presence is always with me'.

In those troubled times of his youth, Duncan had found lonely solace in swimming. 'Competitive swimming is unique. It is the most "psychological" physical sport known to man-

kind. You dive into an alien environment: you can't hear anything; you are all alone. The water has to be your friend. Over time, you develop a feel of it, a sense of touch. And you must be totally relaxed in the water so you can concentrate on exactly what you're doing. You condition your body to a repetitive explosion — the perfect number of strokes per length, the best rhythm and timing — and you also condition your mind by playing through the formula, by anticipating what will happen and how it will feel. In the last ten metres of a race you can experience oxygen debt and your thoughts can get fragmented and wander off. You shouldn't let this happen and just keep your mind exactly on what you're doing.' Duncan is also a master at gamesmanship and in the high pressure world of competitive swimming, his strategies were always unsettling to less tactically-oriented swimmers.

Duncan is engagingly modest. 'Everyone has to be good at something. Just think of all the possible things there are in the world that someone can be good at. A billion, billion things. I had to work at it, in many ways to force myself to win, but I enjoyed swimming and felt it was a worthwhile thing to pursue. I think you are lucky if you find your speciality, luckier if you find it at the right time and luckier still if you find it at the right time *and* recognise it.'

He gives a great deal of credit to his coaches over the years. 'Each of them — Paddy Garrett, Don Easterling and Dave Haller — used very different techniques and are quite different personalities, but even polar opposites can achieve the same thing.' And for Duncan, the apex of his career came in the 1980 Olympics when, having taken the final turn behind the Russian Federowski, he surged through to win by a metre in 1.03.34. 'At the end, I just grabbed the starting block. I knew that I had done it.'

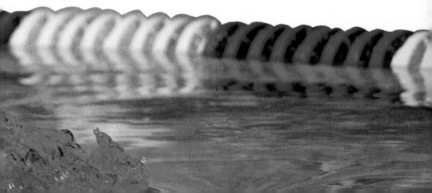

Competitive swimming requires an intensive training programme. 'You'd swim perhaps 40 to 60 kilometres a week and do weight training, running and stretching exercises for flexibility. Altogether it's probably about 40 to 50 hours a week dedicated solely to improving your performance.

'I think fitness for both the competitor and the individual is best looked at by considering balance — the body as a whole. One muscle should balance another. For instance, a swimmer will work to build up the triceps but he should also do curls, a bicep exercise to try to balance the body shape. When he's swimming, the triceps are pulling hard and to compensate, the biceps get tight and fatigue sets in. Also, balance is all important, cosmetically. You want a balanced body shape and not just bulging biceps for instance. Thirdly, cardio-vascular fitness is vital. You need to keep the heart and lungs in good condition because that keeps the whole system well-serviced.

'Swimmers do an extensive stretching routine for twenty minutes or so a day because flexibility is crucial. Then, for general body shape and stamina, we'd do a 45-minute circuit training programme — sit-ups, press-ups, curls, bench-presses, etc. — a continuous set of, say two minutes of each exercise with ten seconds off between them. In that programme, you work round every muscle in the body. You can find some kind of exercise for every muscle and it helps to work on each individually. Early in the season, most competitive swimmers do some running too. It's a different feeling, a different kind of pain, but it's good cardio-vascular exercise and it means you don't have to swim so much when you're working up your programme.

'Weight training with heavy weights two or three times a week can improve muscle specificity somewhat. And in the off-season now, a lot of swimmers find cross-country skiing a good way of building stamina, strength and flexibility. It's a similar movement to swimming — the arms and legs rhythm — and it's done at altitude which is good for cardio-vascular fitness. And most of the resorts have good-sized swimming pools too.

'For the average person, I don't think jogging *is* particularly good, with the qualification that it is good if no other exercise is being done. I make a distinction between running where you're on your toes and jogging where your heels are pounding down. If you jog on roads or hard surfaces, you can even do damage to your joints and internal organs. Frankly, I think walking is a better choice. You can easily walk a twenty-minute mile and there's no jarring or stress on the body. It's a continuous exercise and works most of the muscles in the body and if you just walk briskly for thirty minutes a day, you'll feel better, burn off more calories and have more get up and go.

'It's important, though, to establish a routine — the body thrives on it. If you say you're going to walk half an hour on Sundays at 3 pm, you mustn't let anything else interfere. Just start easy and build up — but no excuses, ever.

'There's a real gratification in becoming fit. It's a challenge fulfilled. And good fitness and body balance make you more attractive to yourself and to others. You're more mentally and physically alert and can cope with stress better, too, when everything is running correctly.

'Balance is important in diet as well. I think we're a bit set in our ways and sometimes eat just for the sake of eating. We can miss out meals quite happily though I do think one should establish a routine and have small quantities of varying foods at regular times. And breakfast is an important meal. It starts the body rolling, gets the chemicals flowing and stimulates efficiency.' In the mornings, Duncan might have porridge (cooked in a slow-cooker overnight) with milk, poached eggs, bacon, sausages, toast and marmalade.

Duncan took part in The Superstars in 1980. 'Five of the seven events I'd never done before and I didn't have much time to prepare for them. I knew I was in trouble so I just concentrated on doing as well as I could. I do like the concept of sportsmen and sportswomen having fun in sporting challenges like Superstars.'

Recently married to Anne, a graphic designer from North Carolina, Duncan is putting his degree in business management to good use with several companies. He is in great demand as a conference speaker and is on the Boards of the Sports Aid Trust, the Sports Aid Foundation (London and South East), and the T.V.S. Trust Fund, and works closely with the Dyslexia Association, for all of which he works tirelessly, fund-raising throughout Great Britain. He was awarded an MBE in the Queen's Christmas Honours List in 1981. His philosophy of life is simple: 'Whatever you do, you get out of life what you put into it.' And Duncan Goodhew never puts in less than 100 per cent.

DUNCAN GOODHEW
chose for breakfast

Fresh Grapefruit

Breakfast Omelette

Wholemeal Toast and Marmalade

Banana Shake

BREAKFAST OMELETTE *(Serves 2)*

1 tablespoon cooking oil

2 rashers lean bacon, chopped

1 slice bread, crusts removed, cut into cubes

4 eggs

4 tablespoons water

salt and pepper

Heat oil in a 15cm-18cm (6″-7″) omelette pan. Add bacon, cook for a few minutes. Add bread cubes, cook until crisp and golden brown. Heat grill to hot. Beat eggs, water and seasoning together. Pour mixture into pan, drawing cooked egg mixture from edge of pan towards centre, allowing liquid egg to run to pan base. When underside is firm and top is still runny, place pan under hot grill until top is just set. Serve immediately cut in half.

BANANA SHAKE *(Serves 2)*

Place 2 small, ripe bananas, 2 teaspoons brown sugar and 500ml (1pt) chilled milk into a liquidiser. Mix for a few seconds until smooth. Pour into glasses. For a quick, nutritious meal-in-a-glass, add 2 eggs with the chilled milk.

GORDON GREENIDGE

Born: St Peter, Barbados, 1950.

Education: Alfred Sutton Boys' School, Reading.

*Debut for Hampshire 1970: for Barbados 1973:
for West Indies 1974.*

*Up to the end of the 1984 season, he had scored 62 first
class centuries, and 5 centuries in one-day
international matches.*

Highest score, 273, D.H. Robins XI v Pakistan,
Eastbourne 1974.*

Gordon Greenidge is arguably the most consistently hard-hitting opening batsman the world has ever seen. In 1984, first at Lord's and then at Old Trafford, Manchester, he pulverised the England bowling, making a double-century on each occasion, and was voted 'Man of the Series'. Yet, but for chance, he might have been playing for England in that series, not for West Indies!

Gordon came to England when he was 14, and England has been his home ever since. His Headmaster writes of him as 'a quiet, shy boy . . . who found classroom work difficult'. But at cricket he excelled, playing for Berkshire Schools when he was 15 — and scoring 50 out of a total of 70 against Yorkshire! The next year, he was selected for the English Secondary Schools XI and appeared also for Berkshire, the side for which twenty years earlier another great international star had played — Peter May, who as Chairman of the England Selectors in 1984 must have watched with mixed feelings the contribution Gordon made to the destruction of the side he had picked.

Hampshire spotted Gordon's potential early, and after a trial he was taken on the staff in 1968. His first year, however, was almost his last! His talent was undeniable, but even Gordon admits that his mental attitude was wrong in those days. 'I was only partly playing the game. I always wanted to bat, but I was never very keen to do the fielding.' His contract *was* renewed, and with it came a determination to be what he calls 'a complete cricketer', and the realisation that he could, if he wanted, make the game his living.

This meant hard work. He played badminton and table-tennis for hours on end, to improve his general fitness. He ran up and down the avenue outside the Southampton YMCA, where he was living, often until after midnight, to increase his

stamina. And on the ground next morning, he practised his fielding.

Gordon's first appearance for the county side came early in August 1970, when he batted number six in an injury-depleted team, making 24 and 18, including a gigantic hook for six out of the ground. Later that month he was promoted (in both senses of the word) to open the batting with the peerless South African, Barry Richards. That was the beginning of a partnership which was to earn the accolade of 'the best opening pair in the world'. They were certainly also the most attractive to watch.

According to Gordon, in the early 1970s he received an enquiry from the England selectors as to whether he was available for selection for the Test side — he was now qualified by residence. He never responded to this approach, for in the meantime, following a recommendation by his county captain (Roy Marshall, also from West Indies), Gordon had been invited to play for his native Barbados in the English winter. The die was cast!

His first Test Match — it was Vivian Richards' first Test as well — was in 1974, West Indies v India at Bangalore. He scored 93 and 107. Since then, he has been virtually a permanent fixture in a star side, while continuing his loyalty to Hampshire, and to Hampshire supporters.

In 1976, on what was a bad Old Trafford wicket, he made 134 (out of 211) and 101 against England — only the second West Indies batsman to score two centuries in a single Test. In 1977, he scored two double-centuries and four other centuries for Hampshire in the County Championship.

However, like all cricketers, Gordon knows too the ignominy and frustration of a run of low scores, when suddenly and inexplicably nothing goes right — the century in his first Test was followed by his being dismissed first ball in both innings of the next match! However, he is realistic, not fatalistic, about such a situation. 'It's something that happens to everyone, and in business too. Businesses go through times of making little profit, or no profit at all. What you've got to do is just to persevere with what you are doing, and work at it until your luck's in again. You mustn't think either that it will go away if you stop playing for a bit. If you do that, your muscles will seize up and you'll be less fit to stand up to the physical pressures.'

Yet, at the start of the 1984 Test series against England, TV commentators in particular noticed a change in Gordon's stance as he moved into a stroke. There was an infinitesimal crouch that had not been there before. It was almost as though he *was* trying too hard: that he *had* seized up, in his anxiety to succeed.

They were right about the change, but wrong about the reason. In fact, he was feeling his way consciously into what he now saw as his new role as an opening batsman and pursuing a different philosophy of batsmanship. He puts it: 'I've found a need now to occupy the crease; to stay there longer and let the runs accumulate. Sometimes you still get the odd rush of blood and play your big attacking shot. But West Indies needed a better start, so that there wouldn't be so much pressure on the lower order batsmen. It was time for me to concentrate a bit more, and bat longer, and in that way get more runs.'

The new philosophy had its first real trial at Lord's on 3 July 1984. England, one down in the series, and having dominated much of the match, were caught in a quandary. On the one hand, what might the master Vivian Richards do on the last day, if he cut loose? On the other, might yet another failure by the West Indies opening pair start a complete collapse? In the end, England left their opponents just about $5\frac{1}{2}$ hours in which to score 342 to win the match, or survive. The critics shouted 'chicken', and settled down to watch the West Indies play out time. They were wrong, almost to a man, about the result — of the BBC television commentary team, only the Indian captain,

The Superteams 1985. Gordon at the bar jump — and playing forward to an unusual delivery!

Sunil Gavaskar, forecast anything but a draw: and he made the extraordinary-sounding suggestion that West Indies would actually win!

The old-style Gordon Greenidge would probably have 'had a go' from the start, and got out. The new model was content to play each session as a separate innings. West Indies won by 9 wickets with 12 overs to spare (Greenidge 214 not out, Gomes 92 not out). And Richards never got in to bat at all!

Gordon's innings, and this victory, put West Indies two up, and really clinched the series. Yet, to Gordon, his double century at Old Trafford, with the series now won 3-0, was a more memorable innings. It underlined both his resolve to play his new role to the full and his team's to continue to be seen to be in the ascendant. It was not the banners proclaiming a potential whitewash of England — or 'blackwash' as some of them announced — that brought out the necessary reserves of skill and determination. It was the feeling, as Gordon puts it, 'that if we were going to lose our unbeaten record, it mustn't be a one-sided match.'

At lunch on the first day, West Indies were 77 for 4, with Haynes, Gomes, Richards and captain Lloyd out. 'We were totally outplayed that morning,' he admits. 'If we'd lost two or three more wickets that day, it would have been all over. You don't see many teams coming back from a position like that.' Still less, he might have added, a West Indies team, with their traditional fragility under real pressure.

Only one more wicket did fall that day — Dujon for 101. And when Gordon Greenidge was finally out, from a rare miscalculation, for 223 — his highest Test score — he had been at the crease for almost ten hours. He had to play himself in, not just at the beginning of each normal session, but also after frequent stoppages for rain and bad light.

Talking to Gordon about The Superstars competition revealed just how much the necessary forms of mental and physical fitness vary from sport to sport. Batting for ten hours calls for different reserves of stamina and concentration than, say, swimming for ten minutes or running for ten seconds in more 'explosive' sports. Being an opening batsman, moreover, represents probably the only form of sporting activity in which success can be measured by survival for an indeterminate period. Such was the strain on Gordon during the 1984 series that for

The watchful touch! Gordon on the way to his double century against England at Old Trafford, 1984.

weeks he hardly slept at all. 'At night I was still on a high — still working!' he explains.

At this point in the interview, enter Carl, aged six, off school because of teachers' meetings, and clearly bored and wishing for attention from father. He gets it.

Gordon has always been a watchful player. But his belligerence and now less frequent bouts of sheer ferocity at the crease belie the private aspect of this quietly-spoken man to whom his family is paramount; whose hobby (and one method of keeping fit) is gardening; and who spends a lot of time on tour reading — his favourite author of the moment is Robert Ludlum, whose latest hardback was being packed in Gordon's baggage for the 1984/85 West Indies' Australian tour. Anita Greenidge, and Carl, and Genna, 9 months, flew out to be with him at Christmas. This was not the first time that Anita and Carl had joined Gordon in Australia. Anita, a cousin of the former West Indies' fast bowler Andy Roberts, is a cricket wife, not a cricket widow, though she confesses that she finds the three-day county game tedious to watch.

For the Greenidges, England is 'home' and likely to remain so for the time being. Gordon's present ambition is simply to be able to settle down in one place with his family. Ultimately, he would like to run his own sports' complex; perhaps in Barbados, where no such facilities exist at the moment.

GORDON GREENIDGE
chose for breakfast

Fruit Juice

Cereal

Bacon and Egg Decker

Toast and Marmalade

Coffee

BACON AND EGG DECKER *(Serves 1)*

1 egg

2 rashers bacon, grilled

2 mushrooms, cooked, sliced

1 bap, buttered

Boil egg for about 4 minutes to give a firm white and soft yolk: cut into wedges. Place bacon and mushrooms on bottom half of bap and top with the egg and other half of bap. Serve immediately.

ANITA GREENIDGE'S
TOMATO AND ONION OMELETTE *(Serves 1)*

3 eggs

3 teaspoons cold water

salt and pepper

½ teaspoon fresh chopped thyme

½ teaspoon marjoram

1 tomato, chopped

1 spring onion, chopped

Break eggs into a bowl, add water, seasoning and herbs. Beat lightly together. Heat a 15cm-18cm (6"-7") omelette pan gently, add butter and turn up heat. When butter begins to sizzle but not brown, pour in egg mixture. With a spatula draw cooked egg from edge of pan to the centre so that liquid egg runs to base of pan and cooks. While the top is still slightly runny, fold over one-third of omelette away from pan handle. Place chopped tomato and spring onion along centre of omelette. Remove from heat. To turn out, hold handle of pan with palm of hand uppermost, shake the omelette to edge of pan and tip pan completely over on to a warm serving plate thus making another fold. Serve immediately.

VIRGINIA HOLGATE

Born: Malta 1955.
Education: Bedgebury Park, Kent.
Junior European 3-day event Champion and member of gold medal team 1973.
Winner, Mini-Olympics, Montreal 1975.
Member of gold medal team, European Championship 1981, World Championship 1982.
Winner, Burghley Horse Trials 1983 and 1984.
Team silver and individual bronze medals, Olympic Games, Los Angeles 1984.
Horse and Hound Trophy as Horsewoman of the Year 1984.
British Equestrian Writers' Association Rider of the Year Trophy 1984

Portsmouth Royal Naval Dockyard — a cold, grey, weeping late-September day, with the wind slanting the rain almost horizontally. On a pontoon above the oily waters of one of the dockyard basins, two Superteams prepare to swim 50 metres to an overturned life-raft, as the first part of the survival test.

First into the water at the gun, with an immaculate racing dive, and first to either raft, is a trim, blonde figure. An Olympic swimmer? June Croft, perhaps, who was due to participate at some point in the competition? No, it was Virginia Holgate — an Olympic equestrian!

In fact, in her chosen sport of the three-day event, Virginia is perfectly at home competing on equal terms with men, and she is a considerable all-round athlete. At school she was in the first team at almost everything, and rode once a week under the tuition of Cherry Hatton-Hall, who had also coached the Princess Anne in first principles at Benenden.

The turning point in Virginia's life came after she left school. She was 16 — 'Too young,' as she points out, 'to go to London to learn how to be a secretary, so I had to stay at home for a year.' Her grandfather, who had bred polo ponies, presented her with an 'inexpensive' horse — it cost just £35. Not having been brought up in England (her father was an officer in the Royal Marines), Virginia had never competed in Pony Club competitions and knew nothing about the three-day event. Now, she 'got the bug'.

The three-day event — its origins lie in the training of cavalry

The Superteams 1985. Virginia demonstrates the poise, balance, all-round sporting ability and competitive spirit which makes her such a fine performer at the 3-day event.

horses in obedience, stamina, speed and adaptability — had unusual attractions for her. 'You have to be good at all three phases — dressage, cross-country, and show-jumping. To me, there's that extra appeal of risk in the cross-country. It's like Formula One racing. To do it you've got to have that little bit of stupidity, rather than bravery — and I guess I'm that way inclined!' There is also the additional difficulty and extra challenge in the unknown factor — how your horse will go on the day. 'On the tennis court, for instance, you've only got yourself to look after and to blame if you lose. If your horse goes lame or just badly, it's your fault, too.'

It takes about four years to train a horse to an acceptable standard. In the Holgate stables are two horses, Priceless and Night Cap, who have competed in team championships; another, Murphy Himself, who is coming up to that level but is still young; and seven others at intermediate or novice stage. Virginia trains them all herself, though she admits, 'Actually, we're lucky if out of six horses we find one which ultimately suits me perfectly. It's like finding a tennis mixed-doubles partner. You might both be brilliant individual players, but you don't necessarily work well together as a team.'

A successful three-day event rider, apart from sheer talent, needs extraordinary powers of touch, timing and balance. There is also the psychological factor. 'At first, I had to learn self-discipline and how to keep my temper,' Virginia explains. 'You can't afford to be conceited, either. Tomorrow you'll as likely end up flat on your face in the mud! Riders have to be humble people, and learn to take the bad with the good. It's a sport in which it's easy to be a winner, but hard to lose. You've got to work terribly hard, too, even if it means giving up a lot.'

Physical fitness is important, too. From January to August 1984, to get herself fit for the Olympics, every day that she was not actually competing Virginia did skipping (700 without a break) or running (15 minutes at a good pace). That was as well as riding four horses! During the season, she avoids greasy foods — no chips or roast, only boiled or jacket potatoes. She eats lots of fruit, yoghurt, eggs ('I'm an egg-fanatic!') and cheese, also meat and vegetables. Though it would not matter for competing if she puts on weight — a horse has to carry a minimum of 11 st 11 lb, which in Virginia's case is made up with lead weights — she doesn't feel hard or fit enough if she is fatter.

On her original horse, Dubonnet, Virginia competed in the Junior European Championship in 1972, the year she started eventing. The next year, on the same horse, she was Junior European Champion and a member of the gold medal-winning team. Further successes followed, and a place in the 1976 Olympic team seemed to be beckoning, when disaster struck. She is disarmingly frank about it. 'I think I'd probably had it too good, too young. I'd had a good run of luck. I think I was getting a bit cocky, and needed bringing down a peg or two.'

The 'bringing down', when it happened, was so dramatic and drastic that it could have been finally decisive. In a fall at a fence in a one-day event in 1976, Virginia broke her left arm in 23 places. So bad was the injury that it was at first decided to amputate the arm. However, five operations later, it was saved. But it was permanently bent, and the hand was paralysed — all but one of the nerves in it were crushed.

The rest of the episode is as much a tribute to sheer grit as to the wonders of modern medical science. 'When I was lying in hospital, I had a picture of one of my horses on my bedside-table. And when I looked around me, there were so many people in a far worse state than I was. I thought — I'm being pathetic. I had to pull myself together and I had to ride again. Without that aim, I don't think the arm would have been working at all, even now. You can do a lot inside yourself to improve your own health. You can't necessarily cure an illness, but if you've got a reason, you can do much to improve the situation.'

When Virginia left hospital, her surgeon's instructions were simple: 'If you want to ride again, you'll ride again. It's up to you. And as soon as you feel anything in that hand, work with it.'

She did just that. 'The first day I felt a tingling in my fingers, I set myself to undo a button. It took me 45 minutes, but I did it . . . with a bit of cheating! I said, "Next week, I'm going to pick up a toothbrush, and the week after that, a jam jar." '

One day, the local vet, on a routine call, asked to see Virginia's X-rays. He looked at them, took hold of the arm then and there — and yanked it straight! In September 1976, six months after the accident, she was competing again at Burghley.

The arm will never be quite right, even so. Holding things is a problem. 'I've dropped a lot of glasses in my time,' Virginia confesses, 'and I can't open a door with my left hand — the arm won't rotate. But it doesn't affect my riding.' Even so, that was not the end of the problems for the Holgate stables. The two advanced horses had to be retired the following year because of injury and illness, and it was a question of starting from scratch all over again to train up two replacements.

Britain did not compete in the equestrian events in the Moscow Olympic Games in 1980. In the two years that followed Virginia's two new top horses, Priceless and Night Cap, came into their own. She won the 1983 Burghley Trials on Priceless, which virtually clinched her place for the 1984 Olympic Games in Los Angeles, always supposing her two horses kept up their form. She had also now been competing as a senior international team member for three years.

To be chosen for an Olympic Games had been Virginia's driving ambition ever since her first international competition in 1972. Just to get to Los Angeles was thrill enough. Actually to compete, to win a team silver medal, and then to make Olympic history as an individual, was more than even she could have hoped.

The Olympic three-day event is essentially a team competition. Personal ambitions take second place. The main rivals to Britain were the Americans, whom the British team had beaten in the World Championship, in which Lucinda Green, the British captain, had taken the individual gold medal as well. In the end, the margin of just three points by which Britain lost to the Americans at Los Angeles — and on their home ground, as it were — was, as Virginia puts it succinctly, 'almost a joke'. What mattered to the team was the way they competed, the way they helped each other and overcame harsh marking in the dressage and upsets in the cross-country, and the reception they got when they returned home.

Not that there were not unusual problems to overcome, too. To build a 4½-mile course on a 400-acre golf-course was, she explains, 'a miracle itself'. To ride it was a nightmare. 'There were no landmarks. Just bunkers and palm-trees, here, there and everywhere. It was like following a rattlesnake. Normally, you can say to yourself, "There's a wood here, a long gallop coming, and so on." Walking the course beforehand, we were worried that we wouldn't remember exactly where we were and that, for instance, a particular fence was round the next bend. It needed extra effort and concentration to recall exactly where and what the next fence was.'

Yet, at the end of the cross-country, the second phase of the competition, while the team was sitting around chatting, someone came in to say that Virginia was lying in the bronze medal position. Thereby hangs an astonishing tale! Virginia, at her own suggestion, had been first rider for her team, a position from which it is unheard-of to win an individual medal. It had been clear that she and Lucinda, as the two most experienced members of the British team, should between them share the first and last positions. Virginia, when consulted, opted to go first, a decision which the selectors upheld. Yet she knew, or thought she knew, that this put an individual medal out of the question for her. Early riders in the dressage have to contend, as do ice-skaters, with judges who are feeling their way and still assessing the overall level that will be achieved. Thus they tend to mark more brutally at this stage than later. And there is an extra responsibility on the first cross-country rider in a team — to act as a guinea-pig and report back on how the course is riding.

By an even more curious twist of fate, and totally contrary to customary practice, the organisers decided that for the show-jumping on the last day, the riders would jump in reverse order of merit *in the individual competition* — to make things more interesting for the spectators. So, when Virginia and Priceless were finally called into the arena, she was jumping for both the team silver and the individual bronze. A bad round could have cost Britain the team silver medal: a single fence down would have lost her the individual bronze. It was like a situation from a film scenario. Indeed, for anyone who cared to remember the dramatic, tear-jerking climax of MGM's *International Velvet,* it *was* out of a film scenario — for on that occasion Virginia herself was acting as the double for the film's star, Tatum O'Neil.

At Los Angeles in 1984, Virginia on Priceless jumped clear. With that round she confirmed Britain in second place, and became *the first woman ever to win an individual Olympic medal in the three-day-event.*

That should have been enough excitement for one year — or even for a lifetime. Back in England, Virginia suffered from reaction and from having, since her return, 'run about as you wouldn't believe'. There was no time to recuperate before Burghley came round again. Night Cap, who had travelled to

Los Angeles but had not competed there, was in good form and, under different circumstances might well, she felt, have had a good chance of what would have been his first major title. As it turned out, he performed well below par at the dressage, usually his best phase, at the end of which they were lying third. That seemed to be that as far as winning was concerned, for ahead of them were two of the gold-winning American Olympic team.

Yet, after the cross-country, Virginia was in the lead, having completed the course within the time-limit without a fault. Even so, such was the congestion at the top of the leader-board that a single fence down in the show-jumping could have dropped her from first to eighth place in the final reckoning.

On that last day, Night Cap performed faultlessly over the practice jumps. Once inside the arena, however, he seemed mesmerised by the crowds and the flapping of tents and flags. He hit three fences, not hard enough to knock them down, but quite hard enough even for Virginia's sturdy heart to 'lose five beats'. It *was* a clear round, and on a thoroughbred, which is a horse of a more nervous dispositon than others. With it, Virginia became the first rider to win Burghley two years running.

Virginia has now been competing in three-day events for twelve years, but reckons she still has a lot to learn: also that much of her success has been due to luck and to the support and practical help of others — her mother in particular, the girl grooms at the stables, and her sponsors, British National Insurance. She and her mother have been on their own, now, for four years since the death of her father from multiple sclerosis at the early age of 56 — he too was a fine sports' player. Her mother's role in Virginia's riding career has been purely a supportive one. She has never pushed her daughter. She has helped Virginia to the utmost in whatever she has wanted to do, but never complains or criticises when mistakes have led to failure. Parents of potential Superstars might well take note!

No-one could withstand the pressures of such a strenuous, nerve-wracking and sometimes dangerous sport without being able to relax sometimes. One reason why Virginia has done so well at it is perhaps that she *always* feels relaxed. She sleeps and she eats well: she enjoys herself, especially in the two months which are for her 'out of season'. She has lots of interests outside sport, including antiques and reading. She always reads for half-an-hour in bed before going to sleep — two favourite authors at the moment are Sidney Sheldon and Jack Higgins, but she admits to reading 'almost anything'.

Apart from wanting to do well just once at Badminton, which is near where she lives, Virginia is understandably vague about the future. On the other hand, with her looks, intelligence, personality, selflessness, determination, calmness under pressure, physical courage, abililty to make split-second decisions, articulateness, and record of success in what was originally a male prerogative, she might make an excellent Prime Minister!

VIRGINIA HOLGATE
chose for dinner

Watercress Soup

Cheese Soufflé
Tomato and Chive Salad
Mixed Green Salad

Baked Fruit Custard

Apple Juice

WATERCRESS SOUP *(Serves 4)*

50g (2oz) butter

1 onion, sliced

2 bunches watercress, washed, roughly chopped

2 medium-sized potatoes, diced

375ml (³⁄₄pt) chicken stock

250ml (½pt) milk

salt and freshly ground black pepper

Melt butter in a large saucepan and gently cook onion, watercress and potato for about 8-10 minutes until onion is soft but not browned. Add stock, milk and seasoning. Bring to the boil and simmer for 30 minutes, stirring occasionally. Purée soup in a blender or through a sieve. Taste and adjust seasoning. Return to pan and re-heat.

VIRGINIA HOLGATE'S CHEESE SOUFFLÉ
(Serves 4)

50g (2oz) butter

50g (2oz) flour

250ml (½pt) milk

1 tablespoon Parmesan cheese

125g (5oz) mature Cheddar cheese, grated

1 teaspoon Dijon mustard

1 teaspoon grated nutmeg

salt and freshly ground black pepper

4 eggs, separated

Set oven at 190°C (375°F) gas mark 5.

Butter a 1 litre (2pt) soufflé dish. Melt butter in saucepan over a gentle heat. Add flour and cook for a few minutes. Gradually add milk, keeping mixture smooth. Bring to the boil, stirring continuously. Cook for 3 minutes, still stirring. Add the cheese, mustard, nutmeg, salt and pepper. Beat the yolks into the cooked sauce. Whisk the whites until stiff but not dry. Stir 1 tablespoon into the sauce, then fold in the remainder. Turn lightly into soufflé dish. Bake in the middle of the oven for 40-45 minutes, until brown and firm to the touch. Serve immediately with Tomato and Chive Salad and Mixed Green Salad.

BAKED FRUIT CUSTARD *(Serves 4)*

4 kiwi fruit
4 eggs (or 2 whole eggs and 2 egg yolks)
25g (1oz) caster sugar
500ml (1pt) milk

Set oven 160°C (325°F) gas mark 3.

Divide fruit between individual ovenproof dishes, reserving a few slices for decoration. Beat eggs and caster sugar together. Heat milk to just below boiling and stir gradually into eggs. Strain into dishes and stand in a baking tin with warm water halfway up their sides. Bake for 25-30 minutes until custard is just set. Decorate with slices of fruit.

BRIAN HOOPER

Born: Woking, Surrey, 18 May 1953.
Education: Borough Road College.
Commonwealth Games 1974 and 1978, bronze medal, pole vault.
Eight Nations Games 1980, gold medal.
Married.
Sports Consultant.

Contrary to some people's early judgments, Brian Hooper has done remarkably well in his chosen event, the pole vault. His impressive record of seventeen improvements on the indoor British record and seventeen improvements on the outdoor British record between 1976 and 1980 is still unmatched. Always a determined young man, his commitment, drive and effort to achieve his self-set goals have confounded many observers in the past — and are still doing so.

'When I was ten or eleven, I wanted to be a professional football player. But I gradually grew disinterested in team sports and was more drawn to individual events where, whatever happens, win, lose or draw, it's down to you. My sister belonged to the local athletics club and our whole family would always go to watch. One time, I saw some guys doing the pole vault and thought it looked like fun. We had a long garden at home — about 150 feet — where I used to practise whatever sport had taken my fancy — soccer, javelin throwing, the high jump at that time. So, one afternoon, I borrowed the prop from Mom's washing line — Mom and Dad had gone out at the time! — and used it as a pole and tried a vault. As soon as I'd done it once, I was hooked and I thought, "I'm going to keep at this 'cause I really like it".

'When Mom and Dad came home, I was really excited and came running in to tell them I'd cleared 4' 9"! Dad said, "That's a terrific high jump, Brian," and I told him, "no, it's on the pole vault." "Oh," he said and I was really disappointed then because I thought it was a major achievement.

'My family was really supportive, though, and for two years I just trained in our garden. We'd go into the woods and cut down some pine saplings, skin them and whittle them down for poles. They'd last about three or four months before they'd dry out and break.

'When I was about thirteen or fourteen, a teacher at school

came up to me and told me I was ready for the district and county competitions. I came second in each and the following year, joined the Woking Athletic Club and started competing. We didn't have a lot of members then so we all did a bit of everything — I'd do 100 metre sprints, shot, discus, hammer, long jump and relays, for instance. That was really good experience and quite interesting too, because the pole vault is really like sprinting, jumping and gymnastic events combined.

'My dad took me up to see a pole vault coach in London but he said I wasn't any good. I was just a scrap of a kid — only $9\frac{1}{2}$ stone when I first started competing — and a late developer, I guess. Anyway I got over the disappointment and decided to coach myself. Dad is an enthusiastic optimist and was really behind me all the way. When I would train, he'd be my eyes and tell me how it looked. Now he's a national pole vault coach.

'Pole vaulting is really exhilarating. It's a bit like trampolining — there's a feeling of flight to it. And there's always a challenge to it because no matter how well you do, there's always the next height to get over. The Eight Nations Games in Peking in 1980 were really exciting. Keith Stock was in superb form and, between us, we improved on the record seven times.

Gold at Peking! Brian in action in 1980.

It was a tremendous competition with each of us seemingly urging on the other to surpass our own personal bests.

'John Pennel and Bob Seagren, both American and world record holders in the pole vault, were early heroes of mine. And I learned a lot from Peter Gabbet, the first 8000 point decathlete. He sort of toughened up my attitude toward training by just making it very clear that if you want to achieve something, this is what you have to do. And Mike Bull taught me a lot about the folklore and history of pole vaulting as well as technical skill. When I was seventeen, I had a sports scholarship to Crystal Palace and when Mike came there to train for about six weeks, I practically lived in his pocket.

'I think it's really important to get a good grounding in technique, to get it right from the beginning. After a few months, habits get ingrained and all you can ever do is improve on them. And you need to be really determined, irrespective of size or shape or physical attributes. Anything is possible for a man with faith.

'Speed and strength and agility are all required in pole vaulting. And courage, too, because it's pretty daunting to stand at the end of the runway, run down it full tilt, stick your pole in the ground and take off! And there is no one physical type though lots of pole vaulters now are over six feet. Pole vaulting is a sport where the smaller gymnastic-type man can compete nearly as well as the taller sprinter type. I'm only 5′ 9″!

'Your training has to reflect all the components of the pole vault — sprinting, long jumps, gymnastics for flexibility and weight lifting to achieve strength over body weight. For a sprint workout, I'll run 80 or 100 metres against the clock. Then I'll do weight training, clean-and-jerks and bench-presses, for example. Weight training should really be called progressive resistance training, the idea being that your body will adapt to physical stress and so you work out in a constant state of readjusting that stress. As you increase the weights, your body tries to keep pace and you gain new strength. There is a law of diminishing returns, though since the nearer you get to your physical potential, the more time you have to spend for a smaller and smaller percentage increase, so it becomes unprofitable and you need to change to something else. I also do some gym work — sit-ups and press-ups and exercises on the high bar and rings.

'I spend about two hours a day on this workout. The amount

of time spent in training is directly related to intensity and duration: the more intense, the less time there has to be. You should always work to your maximum.

'General fitness is very important in the pole vault because it's an all-round body exercise and uses a lot of different muscles. I think the best exercise for someone wanting to get fit would be gym routines — but adapted to suit the person. Most people never get started but it really doesn't matter if it's just one sit-up or one step-up or one push-up. What is important is steadily to increase the progressive resistance and to make the exercise meaningful. You can even begin by doing push-ups standing against the wall. It is always possible, given good physical health, to get into shape. You just have to be fairly determined and keep at it. I think one reason women's keep fit dance classes work well is because the participants don't think they are training. The music takes away the thought of pain. If they went into a gym and worked out, they'd probably get much quicker results, but it wouldn't be the same experience. And the social factor is probably important too.

'Fitness, after all, is very specific. There are different kinds of fitness: endurance-related where you're able to perform at a steady rate over time, and explosive-related where there's a massive energy release but over very brief periods. But there are so many sports and exercises — people should try to find something for a fitness routine that suits them mentally, physically and socially — and geographically too. It's no good deciding to take up swimming if the nearest pool is miles away, for instance.

'Anything will do really to raise your level of fitness — even brisk walking for a couple of miles every day. But once you've achieved a level where you can walk that distance with ease, you've got to make it harder in order to improve — or even maintain — your fitness. Your body always wants to normalise itself so you have constantly to change your routine to keep it guessing.'

Brian is also very interested in diet and nutrition. 'Diet is becoming the next area for improvement in both sport and general health. Training methods have improved in recent years — records topple with amazing regularity. But fitness improvement is a combination of training, rest and recuperation. Recovery from training is vital and a proper diet is instrumental in this because it ensures that your body has the fuel necessary for it to recover and to improve and to stay healthy.' Brian eats regular meals of simple foods. 'For breakfast, I'll have cereal with milk, poached eggs, bacon and tomato with toast. That's full of protein which can be digested all through the morning and keep you going right through to lunch. Then I'll have a large cheese or egg salad with a wholemeal roll and, for dinner, I prefer fish, grilled or lightly poached, and vegetables. I don't eat desserts and don't even have sugar in my tea.'

Brian went into The Superstars in 1981. 'I'd been a specialist for 13 years. I'm not a gifted man in the sporting sense and it's really been a case of drive over natural ability. I worked hard to learn inside out what I had to do. You want to know you're not going to appear foolish!' Not only did Brian not appear foolish but he has also managed the first and only Superstars' hat-trick, winning the UK Final, the International and the World in

1981. In all, he has won two UK Championships, three Internationals and the World title.

'It's a pretty varied competition and I enjoyed all the challenges. Some I had a fair grounding in, anyway — the gym tests, weight lifting and basketball for instance. I think my worst event is the shooting but in the last Superstars, I really needed the points and did quite well. Mind over matter again,' he laughs.

'The Internationals were more unpredictable because you travel to another country and all the facilities may not be available. So you can find yourself in the canoeing event out in the open sea with a Force 6 gale blowing.

'The World Superstars is the toughest of all because it takes place in the USA with American rules. And there are twelve competitors instead of eight or nine and you only have seven events out of ten rather than eight. Superstars is great, though, because it gives you a chance to meet lots of other sportsmen.'

Brian has been married for two years to Janis, a PE teacher whom he has known some fourteen years. 'We met through sport, actually. We were both in the Surrey Schools' team for the English School Teams Championships.' The Hoopers live in a charming house in Cobham, Surrey, close to Janis's school, where she is now Head of Department, and near family and friends who regularly turn out to cheer Brian on. After a three year absence, Brian has returned to competitive pole vaulting and is once again the UK record holder.

'Sporting life is short but I'd like to keep on pole vaulting for another couple of years. I think I can do it. I want to see how well I can do given the limitations of being thirty-odd years old and having a limited amount of time to spend on it.' Brian does a lot of fund-raising and gives talks about sport, especially to schoolchildren, around the country. 'I always tell them that I wasn't the best in my school when I started. In fact, I wasn't even the best among my group of friends within my class in my school. But I really wanted to do something and just keep at it. You don't have to win all the time — no-one wins all the time anyway — but there's a big difference between those who give up when they don't win straightaway and those who are always trying. Sport clarifies issues and you just have to keep at it, believe in yourself and keep working — eventually it will come.' And Brian Hooper is living proof that his philosophy works.

BRIAN HOOPER
chose for dinner

Seafood Cocktail

Curried Egg Hotpot
Crusty Bread

Fresh Fruit

SEAFOOD COCKTAIL *(Serves 4)*

170g (6oz) can crabmeat, drained
100g (4oz) prawns, peeled
½ medium-sized honeydew melon, peeled, cubed
4 tablespoons mayonnaise
2 tablespoons tomato purée
salt and pepper
lettuce
1 lemon, cut into 4 wedges
4 whole prawns

Mix together crabmeat, prawns and melon cubes. Beat mayonnaise, tomato purée and seasoning together to make dressing. Line individual dishes with lettuce and place a portion of the seafood mixture on top. Garnish with a whole prawn. Serve with the dressing and lemon wedges.

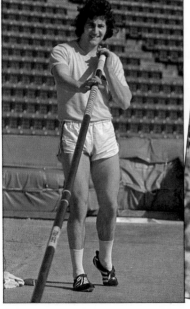

CURRIED EGG HOTPOT *(Serves 4)*

1 tablespoon oil

1 onion, chopped

3 tablespoons curry powder

25g (1oz) flour

375ml (¾pt) stock

1 tablespoon chutney

salt

1 small cauliflower, broken into florets, cooked

100g (4oz) carrots, sliced and cooked

100g (4oz) whole green beans, cooked

6 eggs, hard-boiled, halved

3 large potatoes, cooked and sliced

25g (1oz) butter, melted

Set oven 220°C (425°F) gas mark 7.

Heat oil in a saucepan, add onion and cook gently until soft. Add curry powder and flour, continue cooking slowly for 2-3 minutes. Remove from heat and gradually stir in the stock. Bring to the boil, stirring until thickened. Add chutney and salt and simmer for 10-15 minutes. Add cauliflower, carrots, beans and eggs, mix well. Place into a medium-sized ovenproof dish. Top with sliced potato and brush with butter. Bake for 20-30 minutes, until potatoes are golden brown.

Variations: Try leeks, courgettes, parsnips, turnips instead of some of the vegetables.

BRIAN JACKS

Born: London, 5 October, 1946.

Education: Avery Hill College.

European Middleweight Judo Champion, 1964/65/70/73.

European silver medal 1965.

European bronze medal 1967/71.

World bronze medal 1964/74/78.

Olympic bronze medal 1972.

British Champion — eleven times.

Open Champion — five times.

Married, one son.

Teacher/Author/Sports & TV Personality.

At 38, Brian Jacks can look back on a singularly distinguished career in his chosen sport — judo. To most people, Jacks and judo are synonymous terms. And not only has he achieved honour after honour in the world of judo, his determination and will to win has impressed and inspired millions of people, sporting and non-sporting alike. Yet, as a child, Brian Jacks couldn't run or lift things up without suffering intense pain. His mother, determined to find out why, took him to a series of doctors. Finally, she arranged for him to be examined by Professor Ian Aire, who diagnosed and successfully operated on a hiatus hernia.

Brian was introduced to judo by his father, Albert. 'Dad drove a taxi. And he decided to get fit, lose weight and learn to protect himself. Judo covered them all so he started going to a club. I didn't know he was learning judo and after a few months, he took me along one day. I was about ten years old and Dad said, "You should have a go." So I started practising.'

'Then, when I was 14, I won the London Schoolboy competition. That was a very exciting moment. I'd never won a competition before and I suppose a lot of kids would have given up before that. But I just kept going. The prize was a solid silver medal. Winning that gave me a lot of confidence in myself and I began to get much better.'

Three days before his 15th birthday, Brian left the UK for Japan, where judo had originated at the end of the last century. 'My dad realised that I had potential. He said that I should go to Japan where there were more people doing judo and where I could get better, faster.

94

'He was right. There's about 120 million people in Japan and at least a third of them have done judo all their lives. The sport of judo — or another of the martial arts — is part of the physical education programme in Japanese schools.

'It was strange at first. I was used to Mum's cooking and family life at home and I didn't speak a word of Japanese. But I stayed with a Japanese family for nine months and learned enough of the language to be able to get around and communicate with people.

'Studying was difficult too. Everyone was more skilled than I was and before I became fluent in the language, I had to watch the masters instructing and try to figure out what they were demonstrating by sight alone.'

Brian stayed in Japan for two years. One of his most admired teachers was Watanabe Kisaburo, Champion of Asia who, Brian says, 'was, and still is, the best judo technician, the best stylist, in the sport.' Brian is also a perfectionist. 'I wanted to play judo beautifully, gracefully, cleanly.'

On his return to the UK, Brian soon demonstrated his proficiency. 'Success breeds success. If you do well, you want to repeat it and do even better. There's a lot of motivation in judo. You progress from the white belt (novice) through yellow, orange, green, blue, brown and black, at each stage passing both a theory examination as well as a technical, on the mat, test. In judo, there's always something to strive for.'

And success did follow success for Brian as the cupboards of trophies and drawers of medals in his home attest. 'Most people think of judo as a form of self-defence, but it's not, though if you're very good at it, you can certainly defend yourself.' The 1964 Olympics at Tokyo were the first time judo was officially classed as an Olympic sport. 'That was a really special time for me. I had come home and gone into the national championships and then went back to Japan for the Games, representing my country. I was seventeen.' That same year, Brian won the European Championship, becoming the first British judo player ever to achieve such a title.

Brian is a doer. His list of accomplishments in more than 3000 competitions around the world is acknowledgement of both his skill and his will to win. 'I've always admired anyone who was really good at something. I try to imitate them. If someone else can do it, I can do it. It's just a matter of practice. In fact,

Towards a world record at the arm-dip, Superstars 1979.

I don't think there's any such thing as natural ability. Anyone can be an athlete. Some people do have more awareness of their own body movements, consciously or not. My dad, for instance, has a lot of kinaesthetic awareness — he's a very skilful judo player and when he swims, he swims gracefully. It's a sense of rhythm, timing and style.'

When he was competing in judo, Brian trained every day for

97

On the way to the Superstars 1979 title.

four to five hours. 'Judo is a sport that really exercises all the muscles in your body — you're pulling, pushing, twisting, turning left and right, bending and stretching. A judo contest lasts six to ten minutes and it's non-stop fighting, very aggressive and very fast.

'I wasn't a natural judo player. But I believe in myself. I wanted to win for the personal satisfaction of proving that I was better than other people.'

So when the invitation came to appear in The Superstars in 1978, Brian was determined not just to do well, but to win. 'I wanted to show people that someone who did judo could be a good all-round sportsman too!'

Characteristically, Brian began an intensive training programme. Every day, for six hours a day, for six weeks, he and his younger brother, Shayne, went to Crystal Palace to work out. 'We'd arrive at 7.00 am and cycle for an hour, then go out canoeing on the lake from 8.00 to 9.00. Breakfast from 9.00 to 10.00 was followed by, say, basketball for an hour. Then, we'd do gym exercises from 11.00 to 12.00, weightlifting from 12.00 to 1.00 followed by an hour swimming in the pool.'

His training paid off. Not only did Brian win the 1979 British championship but he also went on to take the European title. He repeated his indisputable double success in 1980. In the World Superstars Finals in the Bahamas in March of that year, Brian finished third, hampered by an unfortunate accident during the bicycle race, but he did become the first ever British sportsman to win two events in the World Final and in the gym test, set a new world record of 118 squat-thrusts in 60 seconds.

In June 1980, he competed in a special Superstars programme called 'Challenge of the Champions'. His damaged knee plagued him again but he broke the record for arm dips, performing 101 in 60 seconds, and set a new British and European Superstars gym-test record.

Fitness is an intrinsic part of Brian's life. 'I'm the same weight now as I was at 21.' His compact, muscled body is still finely-tuned though he hasn't played judo competitively since late 1983. 'Running is the best way to maintain stamina and fitness. I couldn't run around a track to save my life but running in the countryside is another story. You can look at the trees and birds and cows while you're running.' Just 50 metres from the Jacks's comfortable home in Orpington, Kent, the countryside beckons. 'There are country lanes here that go for miles and miles and a golf course with lots of space. I used to go out with my dog, Teto, and we'd run from five to fifteen miles a day.' Teto, Brian's German Shepherd, who has been dozing in the corner, raises his head attentively at the sound of his name, and then goes back to sleep, no doubt dreaming of chasing rabbits in green fields!

'Fitness is here to stay too. People are becoming more aware of what they eat and that they've got to be fit to run for a bus or play football on Sundays. And when somebody gets fitter, he feels better and has more energy and wants to do more things so I think this fitness awareness is going to last.'

Perhaps because of his high level of physical fitness, Brian has always eaten well and sensibly. 'When you're in training, you book regular meal times into your schedule. I'm not a real health-food fanatic, though I often have muesli at breakfast, for instance. I'm not really a dessert person either and don't eat cream cakes or things like that.'

Brian loves cooking and not surprisingly, Eastern food figures prominently in the Jacks's menus. Brian is also fond of Japanese food and the Jacks often have meat which has been marinated in a soy-ginger combination with boiled rice and Japanese pickles.

Brian and his wife, Julie, have been married for 12 years and have a delightful five-year-old son, Brian Philip. Julie helps Brian run his business from their home. Author of three books on judo, Brian is very active doing television appearances and promotional work around the country. He also runs his own judo club in Orpington where he teaches about 150 children every week. 'Judo is a character-building sport. Kids learn to let their aggression out on the mat.'

Brian Jacks is living proof that the sky's the limit when you set your mind to it. 'Sport is cruel — there are always more people who lose than win. Your goals in life are constantly changing. But it doesn't matter how old you are, there's always some sport you can do, and do well. Everything I do, I try to do properly. Excuses are not my style. That's what life is all about really, doing everything to the best of your ability.'

BRIAN JACKS
chose for dinner

Continental Egg Starter

Fillet of Beef in Pepper Cream Sauce
New Potatoes
Mushrooms and Courgettes

Baked Bananas

CONTINENTAL EGG STARTER *(Serves 4)*

1 tablespoon oil

1 medium-sized onion, chopped

½ head celery, washed, cut into pieces 4cm (1") long

1×397g (14oz) can tomatoes

½ teaspoon mixed herbs

salt and pepper

4 eggs

Heat oil in a saucepan, add onion and celery. Fry for about 5 minutes until onion is soft but not brown. Add tomatoes, herbs and seasoning and cook for a further 15 minutes until most of the liquid has evaporated. Meanwhile, boil eggs for about 4 minutes to give a firm white and soft yolk: cut into wedges. Place celery mixture onto individual serving plates and top with eggs.

FILLET OF BEEF IN PEPPER CREAM SAUCE *(Serves 4)*

4 fillet steaks

2 cloves garlic, crushed

salt and freshly ground black pepper

50g (2oz) butter

1 medium-sized green pepper, de-seeded, sliced

1 medium-sized red pepper, de-seeded, sliced

1 tablespoon lemon juice

2 tablespoons Worcestershire sauce

125ml (¼pt) single cream

Season steaks with garlic, salt and pepper. Melt 25g (1oz) butter in a frying pan and fry steaks over a high heat for 2-3 minutes on both sides or longer if desired. Place on serving dish and keep warm. Melt remaining butter and cook peppers gently until just soft. Add lemon juice, Worcestershire sauce and cream and heat gently. Adjust seasoning and pour sauce over

steaks. Serve with new potatoes, lightly cooked, sliced courgettes and sautéed whole button mushrooms.

BAKED BANANAS *(Serves 4)*

4 ripe bananas, peeled, halved lengthwise

50g (2oz) soft brown sugar

juice of 1 lemon

Set oven 190°C (375°F) gas mark 5.

Place bananas, cut side down, in shallow baking dish. Sprinkle
with sugar and pour lemon juice over top. Cover dish and bake
for 20-25 minutes.

BRIAN JACKS'
CHINESE STIR FRY
(Serves 2)

225g (8oz) pork fillet

2 medium-sized carrots

1 small pepper, de-seeded

1 medium-sized leek

1 tablespoon sesame seed oil

100g (4oz) egg noodles, cooked as instructed on packet

1 teaspoon chilli powder

1-2 teaspoons soy sauce

2 eggs, beaten

salt and pepper

Cut pork fillet, carrots, pepper and leek into even-sized thin
strips. Heat oil in a 20cm-23cm (8"-9") frying pan over a
medium heat. Add pork and cook, stirring, for 3-4 minutes,
add carrot and pepper and continue cooking for a further
2-3 minutes. Finally, add leek and noodles and cook, stir-
ing continuously, for a further 2 minutes. Add chilli powder, soy sauce and egg. Stir until egg is lightly set. Adjust
seasoning if required. Serve immediately.

BRYAN ROBSON

Born: Chester-le-Street, 11 January 1957.

Education: Lord Lawson Comprehensive School.

F.A. Cup winner 1983.

Charity Shield 1983.

Captain of England.

Married, two daughters.

Professional football player, W.B.A and Manchester United.

It is a mark of the relentless passage of time that when the present captain of England was born, the red shirts of Manchester United were on the backs of the Busby Babes and the icy runway of Munich lay a year ahead. There was nothing especially remarkable in his background, in happier times for North-East football his Durham upbringing would naturally have attracted the attention of Newcastle United or Sunderland and their glamour would have done the rest.

Of his own ability he had never any serious doubts, the problem was more in his physique, or lack of it.

'When I was about 13 I was pretty small for my age and a bit weak. One of the teachers at Lord Lawson, Bill Chapman, set up a physical training programme for me, doing weight circuits, mainly to try to build myself up. He was really encouraging and used to stay behind after school three nights a week just to put me through that training routine. As a teacher he could just have packed up his bags and gone home after classes but he gave up his own time to help me.'

The long awaited growth took place and when it eventually stopped Robson was a deceptive 5′ 11″. The scouts came swarming around the Robson home and he could have had his pick of sixteen clubs. Impressed by the way West Bromwich Albion had received him as a visiting youngster, and perhaps nudged by the fact that there was an uncle in the area who could look out for him, he moved to the Midlands as a fifteen year old apprentice.

He had the strength of will to deal with the competition for places and long periods of boredom which characterise the life of the young apprentice professional. He was required to demonstrate quite extraordinary mental resources when in the space of a single year he broke his leg on three separate occasions. When that happens to a young footballer there is not only the self-doubt to contend with, the question of whether

Beating his man at Rio de Janeiro, 1984, when Bryan led a depleted England team to a surprise victory over Brazil, 2-0.

the limb will ever be good enough to play top-class football again. There is also the loneliness of being excluded, no one is more out of it at a football club than the player with the long-term injury.

These were obstacles to be surmounted. He became an England Youth player and represented his country nine times at that level, being a member of the squad that won the Mini World Cup. Indeed, a feature of his career has been its ordered structure, with appearances for the Under 21, B and full England sides coming in due course. By 1981, given the modern paradox that some First Division clubs are much more equal than others, it was clear that West Bromwich would not be capable of retaining him.

Of the big four, Spurs, Arsenal, Liverpool and Manchester United, it was the last-named who tempted him from the Hawthorns. He was offered a six-year contract, rare in professional football where playing form is such a fluctuating commodity, and the transfer fee was a breathtaking £1,500,000, perhaps the last colossal sum which will be paid for a player in British football. The albatross-weight on the shoulders of such a fee is crushing, it has been known to destroy totally some very gifted players. The payment was made too at a time when the handing-over of such sums was beginning to engender widespread hostility both within the game and from outside observers.

What then did Manchester United think that they were getting for their money? Ron Atkinson was in no doubt. 'He is the best midfield player in Britain — versatile, strong running and strong tackling — the complete footballer.' Robson was relieved of one pressure point, he was not and never had been an out and out striker. He was a reasonably prolific goalscorer, in 227 games with Albion in domestic competitions he had netted 43 times, but he was spared the intense scrutiny such as has recently attached to Charlie Nicholas of Arsenal.

He does not agree that training is an unrelieved drudgery. He is quite prepared to put in the road work, here he is in sharp contrast to some colleagues and opponents who protest vehemently that speed over forty yards at most is all they need strive for. 'Cross country running strengthens the legs and builds up stamina . . . The sprints and stops resemble an actual game so it's good training.'

For Bryan, stomach muscles are a footballer's best friend and he punishes himself in a heavy programme of push-ups and sit-ups. Pre-season training is purgatory, even for a top-class foot-baller, but having undergone the pain, modest training and the games themselves should keep a player in trim in the playing season. 'It's important that you build up your fitness gradually, though. I suppose the best single exercise is jogging, but not too strenuously. Just jog for a while and then go to half circuits — longer runs at half the speed. For someone trying to get fit, abdominal exercises are a good start. Just doing perhaps twenty sit-ups, in groups of five if necessary with a few seconds rest in between, three times a week, can make a difference. Then just gradually increase the number of sit-ups even by two or three each week — this makes the stomach muscles much stronger in a short time.'

Robson possesses not only playing skill but something much rarer, the indefinable authority that has made him a natural choice as national captain. It is true that the tactical impor-tance of captaincy is nothing like as great as in cricket, but Rob-son is extremely valuable for the air of calm competency which he exudes. The fortunes of the national side revived greatly when he came back as captain in the wake of an embarrassing 1-0 defeat at Wembley from the hands of the Danes.

His forte is not so much the scoring of memorable goals as the stealthy intrusion, the clinical finish, the quick recovery in the goalmouth that sees him first to the ball. Looking back over his career, it is astonishing how often his goal has saved a point or won the match. He is not often the luxury scorer who notches three where his side wins 7-1 in any event. That will not diminish his pleasure in a recent rare excursion into just that area when he had three goals in England's 8-1 thrashing of Tur-key in a World Cup tie. If, as seems likely, England qualify for the finals, it is almost inconceivable that Robson will not be one of the major playing influences when they are held in Mexico in 1986.

Already, aged 27, with a reasonable six/seven years ahead of him, he has realised most current schoolboy ambitions. In addi-tion to the World Cup hat-trick against Turkey, he has cap-tained his country to victory against the Brazilians in Rio de Janeiro. He has also scored two goals in an F.A. Cup final, or to be pedantic, in the replay of an F.A. Cup final.

Bryan Robson is in the thoroughly professional and sports-

manlike tradition of such England predecessors as Billy Wright and Bobby Moore. His taste in sport is wide-ranging, he pays strict attention to what he eats. If his diet sounds conservative, he would argue that time has proved the wisdom of it for generations of footballers. Bryan eats plain, wholesome food. 'I lived by myself for a year and I had to cook or starve. Steaks are my speciality but my wife's a great cook.' Bryan usually has two boiled eggs for breakfast, a light lunch and a balanced dinner, Denise's spaghetti bolognaise being a particular favourite. Roast chicken with sage and onion stuffing and lots of broccoli, cabbage and carrots is a frequent home-cooked dinner for the Robsons. When eating out at one of his favourite restaurants Bryan often orders king prawns in a tangy garlic and lemon sauce.

Eggs also figure in the pre-games menus. 'On Wednesdays and Saturdays, if it's an afternoon kick-off, I usually have scrambled or poached eggs with beans a couple of hours before the match. Before evening games, I'd have steak and eggs. There's lots of protein and it's easily digested.'

When the day comes when the legs will not do what the brain tells them quickly enough, he would still like to be associated with football, not surprising, given the length of time he has already spent in the game. He could quite see himself as a club manager, and certainly he could talk about such things as diet, training and self-discipline from a position of considerable strength.

There have been more flamboyant players in recent years. Robson is not a hammer-thrower, he has no macho compulsion to collect a quota of bookings or orderings-off every season. He worked out long ago that he is of more use to his side on the field than seething on the bench or in the dressing-room.

It is an interesting thought that the two sportsmen he admires most are Bjorn Borg and Jack Nicklaus. Both men were noted for thorough preparation, great skill, coolness under fire and impeccable behaviour in front of their public. Quite reminiscent of Bryan Robson, as it happens.

BRYAN ROBSON
chose for dinner

Egg, Blue Cheese and Pineapple Mousse

Fish Kebabs with Barbecue Sauce
Rice

Fresh Fruit Flan

EGG, BLUE CHEESE AND PINEAPPLE MOUSSE *(Serves 4)*

4 eggs, hard-boiled, chopped

50g (2oz) blue cheese, crumbled

100g (4oz) pineapple, chopped

4 tablespoons mayonnaise

salt and pepper

1 teaspoon Worcestershire sauce

5g (⅛oz) gelatine (dissolved as directed on packet in 4 tablespoons water)

125ml (¼pt) double cream

1 egg white

Mix together eggs, blue cheese, pineapple, mayonnaise, seasoning and Worcestershire sauce. Add gelatine. Whisk cream until just thick and fold into egg mixture. Whisk egg white until stiff and carefully fold into mixture. Pour mixture into individual dishes or dampened ¾ litre (1½pt) ring mould. Chill until firm. Garnish with cucumber slices and parsley. Serve with crackers or toast.

FISH KEBABS WITH BARBECUE SAUCE
(Serves 4)

4 mackerel or herring, cleaned, filleted

1 large green pepper, de-seeded, cut into 8×5cm (2″) squares

4 tomatoes, halved

SAUCE

250ml (½pt) fish or chicken stock

125ml (¼pt) tomato ketchup

2 tablespoons Worcestershire sauce

2 tablespoons wine vinegar

2 tablespoons brown sugar

2 tablespoons tomato purée

Pre-heat grill. Cut each fish into 4 crosswise. Thread onto skewers alternating with pepper and tomatoes. Make sauce by mixing all ingredients together. Place over a gentle heat to cook through. Place kebabs under grill and cook for 10 minutes turning skewers and basting with some of the sauce. Serve kebabs on bed of rice and garnish with lemon wedges. Serve reheated sauce separately.

FRESH FRUIT FLAN *(Serves 4)*

225g (8oz) cream cheese

1 tablespoon lemon juice

4 individual cooked pastry cases

225g (8oz) strawberries, halved

3 tablespoons strawberry jam

Mix together cream cheese and lemon juice. Spread on base of pastry cases. Arrange strawberries, cut side up, on top. Melt strawberry jam and pour over.

ANDY RUFFELL

Born: London, 8 May 1966.
Education: Mcentee Senior High, Walthamstow, London.
UK BMX Champion 1981, 1982, 1983.
UK BMX Freestyle Champion 1983.
Single.
BMX Racer.

Andy Ruffell is a stocky 18-year-old who looks as though he could well be a welter-weight boxing championship contender or a karate expert. He exudes a compact competitiveness. In fact, he is famous for doing things with a bicycle which are rarely seen outside Hollywood stunt circles.

BMX means Bicycle Motor Cross and is a form of bicycle racing which is winning thousands of adherents in the UK. Andy — at 5′ 8″ and 10st 7lb — he is the smallest competitor in the Superclass rating — has won the UK championship three years in a row. He also possesses the ability to push his equally sturdy bike through the air as though it were an ugly seagull.

One misty afternoon in Ireland he pedal-powered his bicycle to set a new world 'body-jump' record for the maximum number of volunteers cleared. It was the act of a supremely fit young man who also likes to have fun.

Andy had ridden ordinary bicycles as a child but invariably they ended up bent, bashed or broken from his incorrigible desire to take them where they were not meant to go. 'One day in 1980, I was carrying the two pieces of yet another casualty of my escapades when I walked by a shop that had a new red and silver BMX bicycle in the window. I decided then and there I had to have it so I got myself a job working in the local hardware store after school and full-time during school holidays. When I'd saved enough money, I went to the store and bought it!'

Such single-mindedness is a keynote of Andy Ruffell's ebullient personality. And it has taken him to the top of what, in the UK, is a very new sport. BMX racing started in the USA in the early 1970s but filtered over to this country about ten years later. The bicycles are specifically designed for off-road racing and have chrom-moly alloy frames specially strengthened by careful welds where the tubes are joined. Light in weight, BMX machines are extremely tough and capable of standing up to the roughest treatment.

Andy quickly immersed himself in the BMX world and in Jan

uary 1981 was asked to ride for Ammaco/Mongoose, the company initially responsible for importing BMXs to the UK. BMX races are run on specially-built courses, full of twists and turns and hills and bumps, over a varying length from 200 to 800 yards. Usually eight competitors tear out of the starting position and jockey for position over the course; races are very fast and competitors do sometimes become unseated but accidents are rare. The bike's sharp edges are well-padded and riders wear crash helmets, gloves and knee and elbow guards for protection.

The BMX season in the UK runs from March to October and meets are held once or twice a week all over the country. Andy has collected an astonishing mass of trophies — over 300 — from these competitions. Particularly memorable to Andy is a gleaming 6-foot-high one which he won at a competition in Detroit, Michigan, USA when he was 15. Not only did Andy triumph over the talents of many more-experienced American boys, but it was also his very first trip outside the UK. 'Before then, I'd never even been to the Isle of Wight!'

Andy practises four to five hours every day, honing his natural ability. 'For BMX racing,' he says, 'you need to be a good bike rider and have a positive mental attitude.'

But pedal power is all important. 'When you're riding, you're the engine,' says Andy. So overall physical fitness is an important component of Andy's general training. Strong and supple arms and legs are vital. Andy couples regular workouts in the gym lifting weights and doing push-ups with swimming and squash games. 'But the best exercise for general fitness is running. I run five miles every evening without fail.

'For the beginner, it's best to start off slowly. Pick a point about half a mile from home and run there and back. Don't worry about how fast you can do it — just enjoy the run. Then, after a few sessions, gradually increase the distance. Once you've got up to five miles or so, start to work on reducing the amount of time it takes you to go the distance. Running really makes you feel fitter and works well on loosening and strengthening muscles all over your body.'

Andy is also aware of the importance of a balanced diet and proper nutrition. 'I don't eat junk food — it's just empty calories. Breakfast is usually a bran cereal with orange juice and French toast. Lunch tends to be a light meal — egg or cheese

*Superteams 1985 —
the power of those
Ruffell legs!*

sandwiches or wholemeal bread with a mixed salad and a piece of fresh fruit for dessert. Dinner is more substantial with meat or fish for protein and vegetables.'

But even with the best will in the world and in peak condition, things can go wrong. Competing for the Townsend Thoresen Trophy in a recently televised Superteams event one of the events was a speedbike relay. 'Each person in the event was supposed to ride flat out to where the next fellow in your team was waiting, leap off the bike and the new man would leap on and speed away.' With Andy's experience at BMX bike racing, everyone thought his team had an edge. 'Well, my team mate came racing up and got off the bike OK and handed it to me. But when I went to leap on, somehow I missed and I fell straight over!' Andy is good-humoured about his embarrassing moment and he redeemed himself in the following year's Superteams by setting a then-record of 104 bar-jumps in the gym event.

In 1983, Andy also won the UK BMX Freestyle Championship. Freestyle is an acrobatic display of trick riding, featuring heart-stopping mid-air twists and seemingly impossible jumps, sometimes to a height of 7 or 8 feet. The feats are graded in terms of technical difficulty and, like freestyle ice dancing, points are also given for performance rhythm and style. It can take anywhere from a few days' to a few weeks' practice to perfect just one trick.

Andy lives at home in Walthamstow with his parents, a sister, Susan, 17, Neil and his twin, Robert, 15, and youngest brother Richard, 10. A well-balanced, serious young man with a genial outlook on life, Andy is determined to make his mark. He now rides a Raleigh Team Special and is very much involved in the formation of a professional BMX circuit in the UK. 'BMX racing has enjoyed a phenomenal success in a remarkably short time.' One reason is that it's a very safe sport and boys — and girls — as young as five years old can compete against others in the same age group. Andy summed up the sport's attraction for him: 'When you hurl yourself out of the start gates, it's a pretty solitary journey and it always ends up the same way — in your own personal achievement.'

As far as the young man from Walthamstow is concerned, however, staying on that bike has as much to do with running five miles a day and eating sensibly, as it has with his innate sense of balance.

'I just don't know why people — all types of people — can't become and stay reasonably fit. That half a mile jog a day for housewives or office workers could make all the difference between an active or a listless life.'

Although he is only 18, the young man on the flying bicycle already knows about an active life.

ANDY RUFFELL
chose for lunch

Homemade Mushroom Soup

Stuffed Jacket Potatoes
Waldorf Salad

Fresh Fruit

MUSHROOM SOUP *(Serves 4)*

25g (1oz) butter
1 onion, chopped
175g (6oz) button mushrooms, sliced
25g (1oz) flour
375ml (³⁄₄pt) chicken stock
125ml (¹⁄₄pt) milk
salt and freshly ground black pepper

Melt butter in saucepan, add onion and cook gently until soft but not browned. Add the mushrooms and sauté for 3-4 minutes. Add flour and cook for 2 minutes. Remove from heat and gradually add stock and milk. Bring to the boil stirring continuously until soup has thickened and is smooth. Season to taste. Simmer for 15 minutes. Serve hot.

STUFFED JACKET POTATOES *(Serves 4)*

2 large potatoes
4 eggs, hard-boiled, chopped
100g (4oz) shrimps
2 spring onions, chopped
2 tablespoons mayonnaise
salt and pepper

Set oven 200°C (400°F) gas mark 6.

Scrub potatoes and prick all over with a fork. Bake for 1 hour or until soft. Cut in half lengthwise, scoop out centres taking care not to damage the potato skins. Mix the cooked potato together with hard-boiled eggs, shrimps, spring onions, mayonnaise and seasoning. Pile mixture back into potato skins. If liked, grated cheese can be sprinkled on top and potatoes placed under a hot grill to allow cheese to melt.

WALDORF SALAD *(Serves 4)*

2 red-skinned eating apples, cored, chopped

6 sticks celery, chopped

50g (2oz) walnuts, chopped

3 tablespoons mayonnaise

salt and black pepper

Place apple, celery and walnuts into a bowl. Add mayonnaise and seasoning, mix well.

SO YOU WANT
TO BE A SUPERSTAR . . . ?

The athletes and sports personalities featured in this book are all, of course, prominent in their sport. They have at least one other thing in common, however: they have all competed before the cameras in TV's The Superstars or The Superteams series.

These events have consistently earned high ratings in the viewing tables for more than a decade. And the reason is not hard to find. Although there is no way that a professional or top amateur sportsman will not take any contest seriously, at the end of the day the Superstars confrontations are — in the words of one of the finalists — 'simply good fun'.

There is something compelling about watching a world boxing champion, who is an ice-cold, fearsome destroyer of men in the ring, apply that kind of determination to a cycle race . . . and fall off the bike. It is equally salutary to witness a judo champion step from the mat on to the athletic track and display an all-round ability of the highest order to become The Superstars champion.

Splendid television, then, and good fun into the bargain. But something more, perhaps. At the base of the Superstars' idea is a concept of fundamental fitness and athletic flexibility which has ramifications for everyone.

It was this thought which impressed Townsend Thoresen, when the company first began to sponsor The Superstars TV series. The company's involvement was logical enough in an age when commercial sponsorship can sometimes seem irrational to the point of perversity. Here was no tobacco company urging exercise and the good life; but the leading cross channel car ferry operator, depending for much of its existence on families holidaying abroad with their own transport, supporting this highly entertaining series which, in turn, depended upon self-motivation and the kind of basic fitness which linked well with the outdoors. A logical match, in fact.

But the Townsend Thoresen management decided that, although the commercial benefits of the Superstars sponsorship were real and very acceptable, the basic idea was capable of extension directly into the lifestyle of ordinary people — and, more particularly, of children.

So it was that the Townsend Thoresen Young Superstars Badge Award Scheme was born. It's a simple idea which takes

The Superstars' non-specialist, multi-disciplined approach to fitness and sports and packages it into a workable project for schools and, now, sports and leisure centres.

The scheme was introduced in February 1984, with a £300,000 budget over a three year launch programme. A few months later, more than two million children, representing 16,000 schools in the UK, joined and the Townsend Thoresen management had decided to extend the scheme to young people who attend sports and leisure centres.

The scheme aims at encouraging youngsters between the ages of 8 to 18, even those who are not sports' minded, to achieve success in a wide range of leisure and physical pursuits.

There are three levels of awards — bronze, silver and gold — split into seven age groups between 8 and 18. Participants can choose to achieve standards for their age group in up to 21 sports which cover five disciplines, including Target and Games skills through to Speed and Endurance tests. Seniors who have achieved a gold award are also able to enter a nationwide Victor and Victrix Ludorum competition — the ultimate test of all-round sports ability.

The success of the scheme, the quality of the people advising on its operation — they include Lynn Davies, Manager of Britain's 1984 Olympic team, Ron Pickering, distinguished TV

commentator and coach, and practising school teachers and sports' organisers David Couling and Doug Dickinson — plus the fundamental altruism underlying it, has been recognised and praised.

In the words of Dickie Jeeps, chairman of the Sports Council: 'The Young Superstars "Badge Award Scheme" is a unique sporting scheme for youngsters and because of its non-specialist, multi-discipline approach, I am not surprised it has been so warmly welcomed in schools and colleges throughout the UK.'

No-one is pretending that the Young Superstars' idea is going to build a race of British Supermen and Superwomen. Nevertheless, there must be *some* reason why smaller nations like Australia and Canada regularly do so much better than the UK in international games' events. There must be *some* way outside medicine of reducing the scourges of heart disease and other illnesses related to obesity and inactivity. There must be *some* way of introducing the joys of sporting competition to children who show no aptitude for particular ball games and traditional, specific track events.

Anyone want to be a Superstar . . .?

INDEX OF RECIPES